the
pollution paradox

J. I. BREGMAN
and
SERGEI LENORMAND
of
IIT Research Institute

A SPARTAN BOOK

BOOKS, Inc.
New York and Washington

© 1966

by

SPARTAN BOOKS

1250 CONNECTICUT AVENUE, N.W.
WASHINGTON, D.C.

Library of Congress Catalog No. 66-21911

Sole distributors in Great Britain, the British Commonwealth
and the Continent of Europe:

MACMILLAN AND COMPANY, LTD
Little Essex Street
London W.C. 2

contents

DEDICATION

To our children—Barbara, Marcia, Janet, Kate, Tim, Chipper, and Bill.

preface

TODAY THERE is an uneasiness about air and water pollution, and the concerned citizen is increasingly aware of smog and water shortages. Despite the concern, generated by frequent coverage in public media, however, relatively little action is being taken. One reason for this public lethargy is that most people do not fully understand the dilemma. They may have read something about suspected health hazards of auto exhausts, something about corrosion, something about New York's water shortage, but few persons fully comprehend the pollution menace.

In part, this lack of understanding is due to the complexity of the subject. Nevertheless, when addressing civic groups, I have always encountered a great deal of interest in the subject and both the desire and ability on the part of my audience to understand the present pollution troubles. As a result of such experiences, I concluded that the lack of public understanding is a consequence of the necessarily fragmented and unrelated presentation normally available to the interested citizen.

One night in the spring of 1965 during a discussion with my wife, Mona, I complained about this and also about the fact that few persons had ready access to the kind of information that is relevant to effective civic action. Mona responded with characteristic feminine simplicity and practicality, "Well, why don't you write a book about it in plain English?'

It was a beautiful and challenging idea, but as attractive as it seemed to me, I soon realized that my writing skills were too technical for developing a really effective message to a nonscientific audience. For this reason I asked our manager of public information services, Sergei Lenormand, if he were interested in collaborating on the development of a manuscript. We had already worked together on one semitechnical article on air pollution that I wrote for *Frontier* (a quarterly magazine published by IIT Research Institute), and I was aware of his freelance writing for the *World Book Year Book*.

Sergei was delighted, and we immediately got to work on the project with considerable enthusiasm. Although we both realized that it would be far easier to do a book on either air pollution or water pollution, we agreed that it was more realistic to handle them together as aspects of environmental pollution. Both air and water are essential to life and to modern industrial activities. They are both being corrupted by closely related activities. They both require similar legislative and technical mechanisms to prevent this corruption. And most important, we believe air and water pollution control should both be integrated into a unified program by one government agency.

How are we devastating our most vital resources? What are the human costs and consequences of this corruption? What can we do about it? These are three basic questions we have attempted to answer in this book so that you will not only recognize the symptoms and comprehend the magnitude of this national dilemma, but of much greater import, so that you will know precisely what you, personally, can do about it.

The authors are grateful to a large number of persons who have allowed us to quote them or use material they've provided in addition to those who have helped us in the preparation of the manuscript. We particularly wish to cite the editors of *Saturday Review* and *Fortune* magazine, Wallace Stegner, and Secretary of the Interior Stewart Udall, who have all had considerable influence on our approach to environmental pollution. This is also true of Senator Muskie, the chairman, and members of the Special Subcommittee on Air and Water Pollution whose hearings provided us with a wealth of material. We also wish to thank the public information officers at the Department of

Health, Education and Welfare for providing the photographs used in this book, as well as source material on pollution.

We are grateful to our wives, Mona and Joann, for their patience, understanding, and loyal support in this trying project. We also wish to express our appreciation to IIT Research Institute's administration for its encouragement and support in writing this book as well as for making clerical assistance available to us. In this regard, we wish to especially thank Dr. James J. Brophy and Robert H. Parrish.

Other individuals who have made valuable contributions are Mrs. Laura Fermi and Dr. Franklin Yoder, Director of Public Health in the state of Illinois.

We wish to express our thanks to our editor, Edward F. McCartan. The authors are praticularly indebted to Jan Forst, who has labored long and diligently in preparing the typescript, and to Evelyn Hankins for her secretarial aid. Finally we wish to acknowledge the valuable comments and assistance of James A. Pearre.

J. I. BREGMAN

Chapter 1

look back with alarm

THE SYMBOLS of recent ages in human history are pregnant with ambivalence. Yesterday it was the spectacular and awesome cloud mushrooming high in the atmosphere as it hovered above a nuclear burst. For mankind it meant the promise of infinite power and a threat of final destruction. Today it is a rocket vehicle slowly gaining momentum atop a fiery pillar of chemical energy. For us it now signifies the conquest of space and an instrument for mass terror.

Once our age was symbolized by a plume of smoke rising grandly from the towering stack of a steel mill, suggesting productivity and prosperity, while a tannery bustling at the river's edge hinted at full employment and new housing developments. This industrial euphoria was dramatized in 1945 when a prayer that concluded Norman Corwin's tribute to Allied victory in Europe—"On A Note of Triumph"—inspired a nation of radio listeners.*

> Lord God of trajectory and blast,
> Whose terrible sword has laid open the serpent,
> So it withers in the sun for the just to see . . .
> Do bring sweet influences to bear upon the assembly line;
> Accept now the smoke of the mill town
> Among the accredited clouds of the sky . . .

Today, more than two decades later, there is not only growing concern about "the smoke of the mill town among the accredited

---

* Norman Corwin, *On A Note of Triumph*, Simon and Schuster, New York, 1945.

1

clouds of the sky" but also about sewage mingling with lakes and streams that the "Lord God" sanctioned for trout, bass, salmon, beaver, and human delight. Medical researchers, conservationists, naturalists, and many other experts now realize that the smoking mill means adulterated air and the riverside plant suggests contaminated water. Hardly a day passes without news media and magazines taking note of this travesty. At this very moment, alarms of national crisis are echoing in the halls of the Capitol. The Congressional Record bears witness to the extent of the concern.

The shelves of libraries and book stores in cities across the land exhibit the outraged testimony on the immense toll of environmental pollution in works by Rachel Carson, Howard Lewis, Donald Carr, and Lewis Herber. And yet, despite the damning evidence, there are not mass demonstrations nor picket lines demanding federal legislation to battle a menace that violently discriminates against humans regardless of race, sex, class, creed, or political beliefs. Even a call to arms by America's most effective mover of men and Congressional mountains—President Lyndon B. Johnson, who proposed in his 1965 State of the Union address that we "end the poisoning of our rivers and the air we breathe"—failed to arouse much public enthusiasm or even sustained interest.

This massive indifference is exceeded only by an unbelievable irresponsibility toward the corruption of our most vital resources, though few of us can survive long without water, and none of us—not man, woman, or child—can exist ten minutes without air. One may indeed stand back in awe of this colossal apathy and ask, "How can this be?"

A complete answer to that question would entail a complex social, political, and economic analysis of American society—a subject that has already filled many books—but the most pervading and significant factor is the legacy of a vast and fecund land sprawling "from sea to shining sea." It is a twentieth century hangover from an era intoxicated by the plunder and conquest of an immense continent, then rich in minerals, forests, game, rivers, fish and a sea of grass that was greedily plowed into the soil, leaving the earth naked and defenseless before the ravages of rain and wind. Then the fertile earth seemed inexhaustible, the supply of crystal waters endless, and fresh air infinite. Of course we have taken our vital resources for granted! What reason could there possibly be for concern in a land so blessed with natural wealth?

This myth of superabundance is the single most important reason that air and water are now the most corrupted of all our natural resources. It has lulled the great body of citizenry into a state of ignorance or lack of concern about the fact that both the air we breathe and the water we drink are being poisoned by a criminal activity that annually results in tens of thousands of crippling diseases and deaths.

In analyzing man's ability to affect his environment, Rachel Carson commented: "During the past quarter century, this power has not only increased to one of disturbing magnitude, but it has changed in character. The most alarming of all man's assaults upon the environment is the contamination of air, earth, rivers, and sea with dangerous and even lethal materials. This pollution is for the most part irrecoverable; the chain of evil it initiates not only in the world that must support life but in living tissues is for the most part irreversible." *

Who are the villains in this crime of environmental pollution? The chemical industry has been accused, the city has been indicted, and even our cherished automobiles have been prosecuted, but these are only contributors to a complex and difficult predicament. The ultimate truth is that we, the people, are guilty—guilty of corroding our wealth and jeopardizing our health. Even more unforgivable is the modern corruption of man's legacy, a legacy of sparkling brooks, green forests, and fresh air that has passed relatively unviolated from generation to generation throughout human history. In a highly catastrophic way, we are our own enemy, and only we, the people, can alter the collective and relentless drive toward urban suicide and the assured demise of the wealthiest and most powerful nation on earth.

---

* Rachel Carson, *Silent Spring*, Houghton Mifflin Co., New York, 1962.

Secretary Udall, long a champion of conservation, put it this way:

> The paradox at the center of the American scene in 1965 is that at the very moment man has built an unprecedented pyramid of personal prosperity, he has exploited land, water, and air so thoroughly and thoughtlessly that he has failed to maintain decent standards of stewardship.
>
> The quality of the total environment has declined with each new advance of the economic indices.
>
> We now enjoy an unprecedented level of economic prosperity. New scientific discoveries enhance our material wealth; new technological developments hold greater promise; measured by goods, gadgets, and GNP, or by our adventures in outer space and into the atom, American society is a "success."
>
> But we must face up to one notable failure—the squandering and abuse of those resources on which the public happiness depends. Pollution is the conservation scandal of our generation. Each of us must shoulder a share of the responsibility.*

While environmental pollution problems are only coming into sharp focus in this decade, they are neither novel nor unique to our society. In fact, they are not even unique to mankind, if that is of any consolation. Long before the existence of human beings, the terrestrial environment was contaminated, for even Nature, with all of its virtues and beauty, injects undesirable and harmful ingredients into the atmosphere and the hydrosphere. Dust, silt, volcanic gas and ash, pollen, and the waste products of animals and vegetation immediately spring to mind. But that is only half the natural pollution story. Nature has some remarkable mechanisms for combating and eliminating its own contamination. Natural dilution by both air and water, bacterial decomposition, solar radiation, and a host of various types of scavengers do a remarkably good job of maintaining a reasonably attractive and hygienic environment.

Without the intervention of man, in other words, the ecological balance is beautifully maintained. This truism is at the heart of the matter and should give us insight into our own evil. *Like Nature, man pollutes; unlike Nature, man has done little or nothing to eliminate or neutralize his wastes.* This habit

---

* Guest Editorial by Secretary of the Interior Stewart Udall, *Saturday Review*, Vol. XLVIII, No. 20, May 22, 1965.

must be changed. We must cease to misuse our modern technologies. Instead, we must now use these same technologies to clean up our habitat. That is, short of avoiding nuclear warfare, America's major challenge in this century.

Not all humans—even thousands of years ago—were unconcerned about air pollution, for venting is evident in the tepees of American Indians, a technological advance that may date back as far as the Stone Age. There is no extant written record of such awareness, however, until Roman times when Senators complained about their togas being soiled by the air and Tacitus described the suffocation of Pliny the Elder by volcanic gas fumes. Perhaps the first insight into the link between man-made pollution and human welfare was made by Moses Maimonides, a physician, rabbi, and the foremost Hebrew scholar of the Diaspora. In 1170 A.D. he wrote that "the relation between the air in a town and in its streets and that found in open country may be compared to the relationships between grossly contaminated, filthy water, and its clear, lucid counterparts."

Nevertheless, no known attempt to prevent air pollution was made until the opening of the 14th century when an anti-smoke ordinance forbidding the use of "sea coal" in London was established by royal proclamation. A commission was set up to enforce the code and punish those proven guilty "for the first offense with great fines and ransoms, and upon the second offense to destroy their furnaces." It is believed that at least one violator of this law was put to death by order of the reigning monarch, Edward I. Apparently, the ordinance was eventually abandoned, for another proclamation, making it illegal to burn coal during sessions of Parliament, was issued during the reign of Elizabeth I. In spite of Her Majesty's efforts, the use of coal rapidly increased as wood became scarce and expensive. By 1600, Great Britain produced some two million tons of coal annually, five times more than the rest of the world. A contemporary diarist named John Evelyn acidly commented that "The City of London resembles the face Rather of Mount Aetna, the Court of Vulcan, Stromboli or the suburbs of Hell than an Assembly of Rational Creatures and the Imperial Seat of our Incomparable Monarch". He added that in approaching London one "sooner smells than sees the City to which he repairs". His pamphlet concluded with observations about the effects of this blight on health, appearance, and vegetation as well as to the "Hands and Faces and Linnen of our Fair Ladies and Nicer Dames ..."

The ensuing Industrial Revolution, as evident to the nose as to the eye, gave further impetus to the already flourishing coal industry, and by 1819 the smoke nuisance was so conspicuous that Parliament appointed a committee to determine how steam engines and furnaces could be constructed to make them less of a hazard to public health and comfort.

By the middle of the 19th century, smoke abatement also became a concern for the United States in cities where soft coal was extensively used. The first smoke case on record was filed at St. Louis in 1864. The plaintiff sued for damages against an individual's smoking chimney and was awarded $50 by a judge who declared that smoke was a nuisance. The case was appealed but upheld by the Missouri Supreme Court.

The first smoke ordinance in this country was adopted by the Chicago City Council in 1881, almost 600 years after Edward's historic proclamation. The Chicagoans declared that "the emission of dense smoke from the smokestack of any boat or locomotive or from any chimney anywhere within the city shall be ... a public nuisance." The penalty for violators varied from five to fifty dollars. Months later, Cincinnati adopted a similar ordinance, and then Pittsburgh, Cleveland, St. Louis, and St. Paul within the following years. Such propitious beginnings in pollution control were effectively canceled by the acceptance, if not the fashionability, of mills and plants spewing black smoke at "the accredited clouds of the sky."

Water contamination has been even more extensive, insidious, and devastating in man's history. Water-borne diseases —cholera, dysentery, hepatitis, typhoid fever—have played a prime role in population control, warfare, and the history of nations.

One of the earliest recorded cases of massive death due to

polluted water contributed to the downfall of the Roman Empire. At the time of the barbarian invasions during the fourth century, the sewer system of the capital—clogged by silt and refuse—fell into ruin. Farmlands formerly drained by the Cloaca Maxima reverted to the disease-bearing swamp now known as the Pontine Marshes. As a consequence, plagues and malaria ravaged the countryside, destroying or debilitating thousands of Roman citizens at a time when there was dire need for their services in defense of the Empire.

Although rivers had been used as depositories for refuse and rubbish for centuries, they were relatively free from heavy pollution until about 1825 as inorganic matter was diluted or deposited and organic matter was oxidized. Nevertheless, during the reign of Richard II, a statute was issued prohibiting the disposal of "dung, filth, and garbage into ditches, rivers, and other water courses near to cities, towns, and boroughs." Henry VIII also issued a number of ordinances relating to water pollution, but the objective of these laws was the prevention of navigational obstructions, not the protection of public health.

In the wake of the Industrial Revolution, the odious aspects of water pollutants became evident, and English officials took action to eliminate nuisances offensive to the nose. There was no awareness, however, that contaminated water could be a source of disease although London—like many English and Continental cities—was periodically plagued by cholera epidemics such as one that took 50,000 lives in 1831. A river was thought to be "wholesome" if cattle drank from it and fish survived in it. Consequently, up to the 20th century, dysentery and typhoid fever were also rampant among urban populations. Various forms of hepatitis—commonly called yellow jaundice and now known to be transmitted by water—have always occurred during wartime among large concentrations of soldiers. In the Napoleonic Wars and in our own struggle between the northern and southern states, the opposing armies were burdened by "field jaundice" or "camp jaundice," possibly spelling the difference between victory and defeat at Waterloo, Gettysburg, Shiloh, or Antietam.

The ancient and more recent pollution activities cited here are meager when compared to the achievements of western civilization in this century. The escalation of air and water pollution through the population explosion and urban compaction has corrupted our vital resources with megatons of industrial and residential fallout. The most spectacular and shameful deed is the devastation of the Great Lakes where many of the finest beaches have been condemned as hazardous to health and Lake Erie has been converted into the world's largest cesspool. This pollution is by no means restricted to metropolitan or industrial regions. Crops have been ruined by air pollutants whose source was as far as 100 miles away. Fish and game have been destroyed in all but the remotest parts of this country. Deposits of soot and smoke particles have recently been discovered in the latest layers of the Greenland ice cap, and measurable quantities of DDT have been detected in the bodies of penguins at the South Pole. In the fall of 1965, the National Science Foundation issued a $47,000 grant for a survey of lead pollution in the Antarctic ice sheet to determine if civilization is threatened by massive lead poisoning.

Although abundant evidence strongly indicates that cancer, emphysema, bronchitis, infectious hepatitis, and poliomyelitis, as well as poisoning by arsenic, endrin, and beryllium—to mention a few—are related to environmental pollution, the American public is still complacent about the corruption of our vital resources. Despite the black lungs of urban residents, doubting Thomas can shrug off statistical and experimental evidence by claiming that a direct connection between pollutants and disease has not been proven beyond the shadow of a doubt, adding "the facts are not all in."

There are enough facts, however, for New York's Governor Rockefeller * to point out that for ten miles south of Albany, in the once magnificent Hudson River, "there are no fish, but sludge worms, leeches, rattail maggots, the larvae of flies—the handwriting on the wall to us, undeniable handwriting on the

---

* R. and L. Train Rienow, *Saturday Review*, Vol. XLVIII, No. 20, May 22, 1965.

wall, that warns us to stop polluting our lakes and rivers, to stop treating our waterways as if they were open sewers." He bluntly stated that the conditions he cited have brought New Yorkers to the brink of an emergency in which the health and future of the state are at stake.

Thus we move toward the 21st century, putrefying the fabric of contemporary civilization—that complex and manifold web of mixed blessings which suggests that mankind is forever doomed to generate new evils with each stride forward, each frontier conquered.

Chapter 2

our vital resources

CONTRARY TO popular opinion, the supply of air and water is not endless, and if we do not begin to employ sound conservation practices now, the consequences could be far more catastrophic than the dust bowls and river floods of the past five decades. Clean air and pure water—so often taken for granted —are essential to your welfare and your health every day of your life. If you are fairly normal in your personal consumption, you will have eaten about three pounds of food by the end of the day. In one way or another, you also will have consumed between four and five pounds of water. On any given day, of course, food is not essential, and for a while you can get along without water. To live through this day, however, you must breathe, and during any and every 24-hour period, you alone consume 30 pounds of air. While you often can detect and reject contaminated food and water by their odor, appearance, or taste, you cannot reject air. You must inhale it where you are, no matter how contaminated it is by dust, dirt, smoke, and gases.

Our vital personal need for air, however, is minute when compared with the enormous quantities essential to heating our homes, running our factories, driving our cars, and burning our wastes in a modern industrial society.

About one ton of air is required just to burn a tank full of gasoline in the normal American automobile. As some 80 million registered cars in the United States consume 70 billion gallons of fuel in one year, they use over four billion tons of air annually. At the same time, the human population inhales and expels three million tons.

The combustion of fuels, either for home heating or for industrial use, devours even more enormous quantities of air. One gallon of fuel oil consumes 90 pounds of air while a pound of natural gas uses 18 pounds of air. Burning a pound of coal requires 14 pounds of air. When the total consumption is added up and the appropriate calculations are made, experts estimate that in the United States we use about 3,000 cubic miles—20 billion tons—of air every year for fossil fuel combustion alone.

If there were unlimited supplies of fresh air, as most people believe, there would be little need for concern, but the total *quantity* of air is fixed, and its *quality* is being degraded on a massive scale because of the increasing demand of a society whose population, urbanization, and industrialization continue to expand. Just as water supplies are broken down into discrete units, such as rivers or lakes, so air supplies frequently tend to remain relatively fixed in large masses over locations called airsheds, which are defined by terrain such as mountains and hills. New air gradually arrives in these airsheds while used air is departing. The quantity of air in these airsheds is determined by atmospheric features. Its quality is determined by meteorological factors as well as the amount and character of pollutants spewed into it.

Most air pollutants require a certain amount of time to cause damage, and so the length of exposure in the airshed also determines the seriousness of the problem. Finally, the degree of purity or contamination of the air arriving at the airshed is relevant to its ability to absorb and harmlessly disperse pollutants. Obviously, the more contaminated the air becomes in its transit, the less pollution it is capable of absorbing before reaching toxic levels. Clean ocean air, for example, is contaminated with nitrogen oxides by power plants along the California coast. As the air mass drifts into the Los Angeles basin airshed, it accumu-

lates the organic vapors of auto traffic. Sunshine then triggers
an interaction of these pollutants, which form the infamous
"photochemical" smog that is now a West Coast tradition. Technically called *synergism*, this process also takes place along the
Delaware River where power plants spew nitrogen oxides at the
"accredited clouds of the sky." These react with the pollutants
discharged by various cities and highway traffic in the valley's
airshed.* It is obvious that the movement of air masses and
their quality, especially where there are numerous industrial
clusters, is a national rather than a community problem.

Regarding the atmosphere's capacity to absorb toxic pollutants, Dr. Morris Neiburger, professor of meteorology at
UCLA, recently made the dire prediction that "All civilization
will pass away, not from a sudden cataclysm like a nuclear war,
but from gradual suffocation in its own wastes." He believes
that the villain is the internal combustion engine, that "Mankind will sink to its smoggy doom through inertia and irresponsibility," and that our species will end "not with a bang, but
with a whimper." Although Professor Neiburger's gloomy
forecast is conceivable, the authors of this book cannot imagine
such prolonged, gross apathy. The meteorologist, however,
raises a valid and crucial question: How much longer can we
afford to overload the air with pollutants?

Unfortunately, this is merely one aspect of the contamination
of our vital resources. Pure water is as essential as clean air,
and in many ways the maintenance of water integrity is even
more difficult than preserving the quality of our air. Harmful
pollution by man and nature is even more universally pervasive
in water than in air. Furthermore, the distribution of water
is highly erratic. Anyone who remembers his geography lessons
realizes that large portions of the earth's land mass are unsuit-
able for either industry or agriculture because of insufficient
rainfall.

Unlike air, water resources are not easily tapped, especially

---

* John T. Middleton, "Man and His Habitat: Problems of Pollution," Bulletin
of the Atomic Scientists, March, 1965.

in this age of pollution megatonnage. Even getting water from your faucet, which involves considerable investment in plumbing and treatment, requires more effort than inhaling. The effort and expense of producing clean water, however, does not mean we are short; we have an abundant supply of water. The average annual rainfall in the United States is about thirty inches, five billion acre feet that falls on two billion acres of land surface. In a single day our country is showered by 4,300 billion gallons of water, indicating how America became rich and resplendent with forests, game, rivers, fish, and a sea of grass *before the meddling of man*. Seventy percent of our moisture, however, is evaporated by the sun or transpired by plants and animals. This means 3,000 billion gallons are lost to the atmosphere each day, leaving 1,300 billion gallons for ground water, stream flow, or other forms of runoff. Of this, we are managing or controlling less than 400 billion gallons. Over half of this available water—drawn from streams and lakes or pumped out of the earth—is used by industry. Most of the remainder is consumed by agriculture and municipalities.

Overlooking the role of air, for the moment, industry's most important raw material is water. It is a source of power, a coolant, a transportation vehicle, an ingredient in processing thousands of products and materials, and a cleansing agent. Factories consume water in astonishing quantities—1,400 gallons for a dollar's worth of steel, nearly 200 gallons for a dollar's worth of paper. This means that 65,000 gallons of water are required to produce a ton of steel and 39,000 gallons are needed for a ton of paper. A barrel of gasoline or oil involves 357 and 770 gallons of water respectively. Even the production of a gallon of whiskey requires 80 gallons of water. And a ton of soda?—85,000 gallons! * These industrial uses of water understandably degrade its quality, sometimes making it as unfit for reuse as residential sewage.

While agriculture requires less water than industry, it "con-

---

* Sheppard T. Powell and Arthur D. Weston, "Report on Industrial Water Supply to Task Committee No. 1 of the Engineering Joint Council, National Water Resources Policy Committee," New York, 1950.

sumes" more. Many industries recover and reuse their water, but 60 percent of the water employed for irrigation is lost. Furthermore, the water returned to rivers and streams is often laden with salts, minerals, and agricultural chemicals which are difficult to remove by conventional waste treatment methods.

At the same time, better standards of living and sanitation— laundries, garbage grinders, air conditioners, multiple bath- rooms, lawn sprinklers—increase our direct per capita use of municipal water. For these reasons, as well as population growth, many cities must draw their water from greater and greater distances or build expensive treatment plants.

Indirect human consumption, although rarely considered, is also relevant to our water resources. According to Professor Charles Bradley, a permanent water shortage affecting our standard of living will occur before the year 2000. In an article published in *Science*,* he pointed out that the wheat used to make two and one-half pounds of bread transpires 300 gallons of water. In other words, if we lived by bread alone, we would each need more than 300 gallons of water daily. Obviously our lives are not so simple. The automobile you drive involved thou- sands of gallons of water for the production of steel, aluminum, rubber, and various synthetic materials. Just the paper for the book you're reading consumed two gallons of water. This is minute when compared to eating a one-pound steak. Each day a two-year-old steer weighing 700 pounds drinks 12 gallons of water and eats 30 pounds of alfalfa which transpired 24,000 pounds of water. In water terms, just getting your steak to the table required at least 2,900 gallons of water!

Higher incomes, better transportation, and more leisure have resulted in a national preoccupation with recreation as well as with good steaks. Much of this activity is related to swimming, fishing, and boating. Although recreational use of water cannot be measured in gallons, the growing danger to clean sandy beaches, expanses of blue water, and crystal mountain brooks— which yearly diminish in quality—is highlighted by other kinds

---

* Charles Bradley, *Science*, "Human Water Needs and Water Use in America," Vol. 138, No. 3539, October 26, 1962, pp. 489-491.

of statistics. From 1920 to 1959, for example, the Department of Health, Education and Welfare (HEW) estimates that the number of American swimmers doubled, rising to 60 million people. The number of fishing licenses sold in this period increased from 3 to 20 million. The greatest growth, by far, came in boating; in 1920, less than 20,000 boats of all types were sold, but by 1959, the annual sale had reached 550,000, a whopping 2,750 percent increase.

The changing character of our society is reflected in the changing demands for water by municipalities, agriculture, and industry. Today, municipal use is about nine times greater than in 1900, rising from 3 to almost 27 billion gallons daily while municipal populations grew five times from 30 to 150 million persons. In the same period, agricultural use—most of it for irrigation in the western states—increased from 22.2 to 140 billion gallons each day. At the beginning of the century, industry used less water than agriculture—15 billion gallons daily. In the following six decades, however, industrial consumption rose almost thirteenfold, and it now uses 190 billion gallons every day. This is not surprising when you realize that it takes more water to manufacture a yard of rayon than to *grow, process, and weave* a yard of cotton, silk, linen, or wool.

Do these figures indicate that we are running out of air and water? Of course not! But what is the appearance of the lake or the river you use for boating? What does it smell like? What kinds of beaches are available to the residents along the shores of Lake Erie? How was the view of the city you approached on your way to work? And did you close your car windows to avoid gagging on the fumes of trucks and buses?

Nationally, we are short of neither air nor water. The northeastern states get a generous 40 inches of rain annually—30 inches during recent drought years—yet New York City, which is surrounded by water, is having still another water crisis. While water officials have nightmares on the East Coast, residents of Los Angeles—where the annual rainfall is less than 14 inches—are watering lush green lawns and lolling in thousands of backyard pools. The problem in New York is not a shortage of water; the problem is a shortage of *pure* water. The problem in Los Angeles, smog capital of the world, is not an inadequate supply of air; the problem is an inadequate supply of *clean* air. The water crisis in New York City, the air pollution crisis in Los Angeles, the silent assaults on cities from sea to shining sea, will batter us senseless—as Professor Neiburger predicts—if we persist in corrupting our vital resources.

Chapter 3

the silent assault

ONE REMARKABLE aspect of environmental pollution is the way most of us close our eyes and noses to the filth and foul odors which constantly assail us in almost every city in America. Few take note of the soiled shirt discarded at the end of the work day, of the accumulated grime on the window sills of apartments, of blackened public buildings and discolored residences, of foamy water running from a kitchen tap, of the veil of blue smoke and the stench of exhaust along expressways, of murky and fetid water full of dead fish at public beaches, or of stinking rivers that wind through our cities. These are some of the most obvious chronic symptoms indicating the existence of serious pollution problems. The fact that they are generally ignored or tolerated is a dubious tribute to human adaptability.

Los Angeles is probably the best known example of how we adapt to our environment. People make jokes about the smog in an aerial sewer that irritates eyes and lungs and is now an accepted part of the climate. The daily weather reports include the smog index, and the city, which has been called "a gas chamber," actually boasts of having created the first disaster prevention program in the world to protect the public from the kinds of catastrophies modern living brings into being. Automatic instruments monitor the contaminant levels around the clock, 365 days each year, at eight locations in Los Angeles County. An electronic warning system flashes the news of dangerous atmospheric pollution to a monitoring center which is manned at all times to meet any emergency. The entire county is on a three-stage alert system. If pollution nears a hazardous level, the public is asked to avoid needless combustion and some 450 industrial plants are readied to cease operations. At the second stage, when contamination is distinctly hazardous, the operation of all motor vehicles and plants is limited to only essential activities. If pollution should become acutely dangerous, local control officials can ask the governor to declare a state of emergency and take action under the California Disaster Act. During the first eight years of this disaster prevention program, there have been forty-five first-stage alerts!

Although the severity and frequency of such episodes are caused by the magnitude of the population (over 6,500,000), of industry (some 20,000 plants), and of transportation (nearly 3,500,000 motor vehicles), the Los Angeles basin has had a smog problem ever since humans made fires in the valley. The first known European to discover the area, a Spaniard named Juan Rodriguez Cabrillo, noted that the smoke of Indian camps formed a bluish haze over the valley. Reflecting his concern about the seascape, Cabrillo referred to the area as the "Bay of Smokes," now known as San Pedro Bay. As this suggests, there are natural geographic and meteorological conditions that sometimes seriously aggravate the problem of urban and industrial contamination of the atmosphere.

In the first place, Los Angeles is almost completely hemmed in by a mountain barrier that rapidly rises from the sea to a height of about 1,800 feet. Second, from April through October especially, warm Pacific air masses frequently get trapped by this mountain wall and, if the light sea breezes in the basin at ground level are relatively cooler, a thermal inversion results, inhibiting the circulation of atmospheric air and the normal dispersion of pollutants. When the wind velocity is low, there is little ventilation and the Los Angeles basin is meteorologically sealed as effectively as a jar capped with Saran wrap. Ironically, the splendid southern California climate makes this gas chamber even more lethal, for the sun's radiation triggers

Los Angeles County Air Pollution Control District

Los Angeles smog

reactions that form the ozone and acids of chemical smog. The effect on humans can be drastic, as evidenced by the thousands of smarting eyes, accompanied by weeping, sneezing, and coughing when the fumes spread their irritations throughout the downtown area and into the foothills.

Are thermal inversions peculiar to Los Angeles? Not at all. They are common throughout the United States and, in some areas are known to persist about 50 percent of the time. Even windy Chicago, sprawled along a beautiful lake front, is subject to the thermal phenomenon.

Although Los Angeles has the most extensive and expensive air pollution abatement and control program in the world, the smogs are increasingly persistent and frequent. In its battle against air pollution, Los Angeles County has closed down 1,500,000 incinerators, installed 11,000 pollution control devices, filed 27,574 complaints against violators of air pollution ordinances, and levied more than $726,000 in fines. A few years ago, as contamination continued to get worse despite these efforts, attention was focused on the automobile. Consequently, in 1960 California passed a law requiring all new autos sold in the state to be equipped with crankcase devices. Officials estimate that there are now more than 4,000,000 vehicles in California with this equipment. Another law has recently been passed which requires either engine modifications or installation of exhaust control units on 1966 model cars to meet new limits on exhaust pollutants. Nevertheless, total pollution emissions will be reduced by no more than 30 percent, and by 1975, because of continued industrial and population growth, air contamination will be even worse than it is now. If you fly into the "soup" that shrouds Los Angeles from bright blue skies, you will understand why it has the reputation of being the smog capital of the world. It is an example of too little, too late, and it should serve as a warning to the 50,000,000 Americans living in more than 300 cities that have a major air pollution problem.

The belated battle against smog on the West Coast is matched —indeed exceeded—by a long delayed mobilization for a crusade against water pollution on the East Coast. The water shortage in New York City, mecca of American culture and learning, is so critical that then-Mayor Wagner announced in July, 1965, that he was forced to reconsider his opposition to the installation of residential water meters. He told a radio-TV audience that free water, which he called "part of the social philosophy of the people of the City of New York," might soon be as dead as the five-cent cigar. That same day a Federal report warned that unless immediate action was taken, four of the main reservoirs supplying the city with water would be completely dry by November and that six others would be sorely depleted. The report also indicated that citizens of the Delaware River Basin, which supplies water to New York and Philadelphia, should be prepared for a devastating emergency if the drought conditions of the last four years continue into a fifth.

Water shortage is an old New York story, but an occasional summer panic has never induced a lasting sense of concern. Back in 1950, a pumping station with a capacity of 100 million gallons a day was built on the Hudson at Chelsea above the salt contamination of the Atlantic. It was dismantled without being used when the rains came and the crisis eased. As late as 1955, the city's Board of Water Supply flatly stated that "New York City is assured of a plentiful supply of the finest water for the rest of this century."

The mirage of an endless bounty of free water underlies the flagrant waste of water by eight million New Yorkers and the enormous consumption of 1,250,000,000 gallons on a typical summer day, while seven million Londoners consume only 365 million gallons. Rather than reduce this gargantuan voracity or repair the "leakiest" water system in the United States, New York's response is to spend millions of dollars on ribbons of aqueducts that reach out to Westchester, the Catskill Mountains, and the upper reaches of the Delaware River Basin. Ironically, while half a billion gallons of water are carried 150 miles from the Pepacton and Neversink reservoirs to New York City faucets, toilets, and urinals, 2.5 billion gallons flow majestically by Manhattan down the mighty Hudson and out to sea.

Why, then, is the great metropolis caught up in still another spasm of hydrologic hysteria? Once again the shortage is blamed on drought, for New York has been meteorologically cheated out of 25 percent of the precipitation it is accustomed to. The real problem, however, is a massive schizophrenia induced by public indifference and official myopia. While desperately reaching into the hinterlands for pure, clean water of low mineral content and no off-taste, the city pumps over 600 million gallons of raw sewage into one of the world's once loveliest and most scenic rivers. In fact the water crisis is so acute that the never-used pumping station above Chelsea—originally built for $3 million—has been scheduled for reactivation despite the "sludge, worms, leeches, and maggots below Albany" or the fact that in 1958 pollution of the Hudson as far north as Rensselaer was so hazardous that the County Health Commissioner declared that increased chlorine treatment couldn't be relied on "to provide the long-range optimum protection desired." Not less than ten cities contribute raw human wastes to the river that bubbles crystal clear, cold, and sparkling out of the Adirondacks, where trout fishing is splendid if you are willing to tramp up the river far from the nearest town or highway. Within a hundred miles, at Gloversville, two million gallons of untreated industrial wastes from twelve tanning factories flow into Cayadutta Creek, then on to the pastoral Mohawk River which joins the Hudson at Albany. Gloversville is merely one of 1,167 communities in Empire State known to be pouring untreated sewage and industrial wastes into New York waterways, which are infested with the bacteria, viruses, and poisons of tuberculosis, dysentery, hepatitis, poliomyelitis, diphtheria, pesticides, detergents, acids, and scores of toxic chemicals.

While water in New York and smog in Los Angeles are major concerns, even the city of Denver has been alerted to the hazards of "smaze," a combination of smoke and natural haze. Like most Rocky Mountain residents, the citizens of Denver were extremely proud of their clean mountain air and crystal clear skies. Since 1957, however, air pollution has been evident. By 1964 there were days when a view of the nearby Rockies was

Charles E. Grover

Denver "smaze"

screened out by a curtain of smaze. When measurements of the pollution were made by city and U. S. Public Health Service officials, they found that, surprisingly enough, Denver has an air contamination problem comparable to other cities of similar size.

The following statement by Mrs. Chester W. Rose to the Special Subcommittee on Air and Water Pollution, headed by Senator Edmund S. Muskie, is most revealing:

A little less than 3 miles east of here, on the corner of 13th Avenue and St. Paul Street, is the brick bungalow, common to Denver, in which I have lived for 20 years. When I first acquired this property, it was located in a clean, pleasant residential neighborhood in which it was a delight to live. A thorough weekly cleaning kept the house respectably presentable, and curtains and drapes needed cleaning only twice a year. Several years ago all this changed when 13th Avenue was made a one-way through street and the heavy traffic moving from east to west shifted to this throughway. Since then, although the area still remains a residential neighborhood, everything in my house is daily covered by a black, oily substance which is difficult to remove, the curtains and drapes should be cleaned at least once a week, windows absolutely cannot be kept clean, and the accompanying odor which is usually disagreeable at times becomes almost unbearable. Besides all these offensive developments, we must battle constantly to retain any semblance of a yard. Despite frequent and costly additions to the soil, the grass on the south terrace along 13th Avenue and on the parkway is rapidly dying. As a matter of fact, from an economic standpoint, I am forced to spend more and more money just for lawn care, for cleaning and laundry bills, and for home lighting which is necessary because of reduced visibility from natural sources of light which do not always filter through the thick pollution.

In addition, both my husband and I have developed an eye allergy which the doctors inform us has been caused by air pollution, and my husband has acquired an unhealthy chest condition, also apparently attributable to air pollution. If this is progress, we don't want any.

Part of the air pollution in our neighborhood must come from industry which is located west and south of us, but the very apparent causes are the automobiles and the backyard incinerators. Something can and must be done about all these factors before we all become enervated to the point of nonproductivity.

Similar progress is also being made near Houston, where a multibillion-dollar, manned space program at a multimillion-dollar facility has been created. While the most sophisticated and advanced technology developed by humans—involving electronic computers, rocket vehicles, and interplanetary navigation—puts man into space, one of the most tragic cases of water pollution in the United States is destroying an enchanting and lovely recreational body of water.

The announcement that the nerve center of the massive space exploration program was to be located on the shores of Clear Lake in Harris County, Texas, signaled the initiation of one of the most spectacular booms of industrial, commercial, and residential land development ever undertaken. The significance of the 1961 announcement was immediately realized; space-oriented industries would inevitably gravitate to the Clear Lake area in support of the aerospace program. Developers, large and small, began planning the construction of homes and facilities to serve the anticipated population influx.

Clear Lake is a small and attractive body of water at the mouth of Clear Creek, close to Galveston Bay. The opportunities for water sports and yachting figured prominently in the development of houses and homesites in the Clear Creek Basin. By 1964 some 47,000 persons had settled in the area. It soon became evident that property values would decline as a result of imminent health hazards, threats to recreation, and the destruction of the lake's beauty.

A group of civic-minded citizens, deeply concerned about the growing crisis in water pollution, sponsored a study of the situation. The research team found that the central problem affecting recreational use of the basin water was a high bacterial count caused by the drainage of septic tanks, pleasure boats, and both agricultural and storm water runoff. Inspection of sewage treatment in the watershed revealed that there was poor chlorination of sewage effluent throughout the area, and that in six plants there was no chlorination at all. With few exceptions, the smaller treatment plants lacked proper operation and maintenance. It was also discovered that of the estimated 47,000 persons in the basin, only 24,000 were served by sewer systems. In view of an expected population growth to about 500,000 persons, the report concluded cautiously that unless extensive plans are made for the immediate and future abatement of stream pollution in the basin, Clear Creek and Clear Lake would become unfit for recreational waters, unattractive as a setting for residential living, and inevitably cause a decline in general property values.

Nothing has been done! Control of the situation became impossible when squabbling local communities got involved and collectively agreed not to band together for water pollution control in order to preserve their independence, a philosophy that is consistent with the antizoning policy of Houston. Meanwhile, the contamination gets worse, rapidly transforming Clear Lake into yet another disgusting and nauseating cesspool.

Ironically, many of the residents on Clear Lake are deeply involved with the incredibly difficult problems related to providing our astronauts a supply of clean water and fresh air during the planned voyages to the moon and back to earth. While the Federal government is spending millions to insure drinking water for three men in space, practically nothing is being spent to clean up the mess in Clear Lake for thousands of people residing in that area, including the astronauts' families.

Congressman Wright of Texas summed up the national situation when he said to his colleagues in the House of Representatives:

> In a Connecticut public school, a new student tries the drinking fountain and steps back in horror as a milky substance froths up in bubbles from the faucet. A classmate explains that it's a bad time of day to get a drink, since detergents are working their way back through the city's water systems.
>
> Along the flooding Mississippi River this week, untreated sewage is washed up through storm sewers into the streets of several towns.
>
> In the Nation's Capitol, a father proudly takes his young daughter for a ride in a swan boat on the beautifully landscaped basin where cherry trees form a delicate pink wreath beneath the Grecian grandeur of the Jefferson Memorial. He looks away in frantic embarrassment, a bit sick at his stom-

ach, and suddenly changes the subject when his little girl asks 'What are all those odd-looking things on top of the brownish water?'

We have focused on a handful of pollution problems to indicate what is happening in the wealthiest and most powerful nation on earth, but certainly, if you look around, you can see the same symptoms of chronic contamination in Atlanta, Raleigh, Buffalo, Cincinnati, Harrisburg, Detroit, Gary, Sioux Falls, and Phoenix. You can smell them up and down the Raritan, Mississippi, and Colorado Rivers, or in any major seaport. These assaults on our vital resources, on air and water, are the handmaidens of industrial and urban ambivalence, a 20th century schizophrenia that provides goods and gadgets while attacking the economic and medical health of the nation.

Chapter 4

sources of corruption

FROM THE first to the last breath of life, we are all sources of pollution. With advancing age and enterprise, our waste contributions increase in both variety and volume. Nationwide, our gargantuan industrial and urban operations—fuel combustion, sewage and garbage disposal, the conversion of raw materials into finished products, land clearance and construction— generate megatons of pollutants that burden our vital resources with a massive fallout that is hazardous to health, property, livestock, crops, fishing grounds, and recreational waterways.

Our waste products number in the thousands, and their continuous increase reflects our growing affluence and technological sophistication. Personal human activity accounts for several hundred pollutants alone. Each year hundreds of new chemicals are manufactured, and many of these find their way into our airsheds and waterways. The variety, let alone the quantity, of dangerous and damaging water pollutants is overwhelming— garbage and refuse, feces, urine, detergents, silt, sediments, acids, minerals, radioactive debris, and hundreds of other industrial wastes which affect the quality of our water resources physically, physiologically, biologically, and chemically.

Physical pollution due to substances from metals to dyestuffs can color water and harm the photosynthesis of plant life. Sand, ashes, gravel, coal, dust, and other sediments create turbidity. When excessive, it cuts off sunlight, reduces the amount of

Susquehanna River foam

dissolved oxygen in water, and destroys fish. Esthetically, the most objectionable physical effect of pollution is the presence of foam and scum caused principally by synthetic detergents. Although seldom a human health hazard, even low concentrations of these cleansing agents can be highly toxic to fish.

Physiological pollution by oil, minerals, decaying plant life, and chemicals affects both the taste and odor of water. Biological pollution is a consequence of sewage which promotes the growth of algae and other undesirable marine organisms. Sewage is also laden with dangerous bacteria and viruses of such diseases as tuberculosis, hepatitis, polio, diphtheria, typhoid, and dysentery.

Chemical pollution, primarily by industrial and mining wastes, includes the organic discharges of food processing, tannery, and dairy operations. Fats and oils—also produced in washing wool and laundering—prevent aeration and result in the putrefaction of the organic materials. Inorganic chemical corruption is caused by the disposal of acids, alkalies, and the crushed or ground metal particles that are damaging to fish.*

In these ways, the use, not the availability, of water is being increasingly limited. Along the Atlantic Coast and in the Great Lakes, municipal sewage and industrial wastes have caused public health authorities to close beaches to swimmers and to prohibit fishing in many areas. Enormous quantities of chemicals, acids, oils, greases, salts, and both animal and vegetable refuse have been poured into rivers throughout New England. Miles of streams in Pennsylvania, Ohio, and West Virginia have been ravaged by acid mine drainage. In rural areas throughout the South, groundwater and streams are being assaulted by insecticides and pesticides. In the Southwest, salt brine contamination limits the supply of water for industry and agriculture. In the Northwest, radioactive material is destroying salmon in the Columbia River. These are the symptoms of an impending water shortage, not because of drought or lack of supply but because of the massive corruption of our waterways by municipal, industrial, and agricultural activity.

* G. V. James, *Water Treatment*, Technical Press, London, 1965.

Possibly the most offensive and objectionable aspect of water contamination is the flushing of human sewage directly into our rivers and lakes. This barbaric practice is a relic of the Dark Ages. It should be banned by national law to immediately end its odious and dangerous practice by over two thousand American communities.

Today, 10 percent of our municipal wastes flows directly into waterways with absolutely no treatment. An additional 22 percent gets merely primary treatment which removes no more than a third of the waste matter. Only 34 percent receives secondary treatment, and even the most advanced existing treatment facilities cannot remove all objectionable pollutants. Furthermore, many cities with adequate treatment plants negate decontamination by the use of combined sanitary and storm sewerage. After a fifteen-minute shower over Buffalo, New York, for example, less than a tenth of an inch of rainfall caused a four-hour overflow of water in its sewage treatment facility. That day, consequently, city engineers were forced to let untreated filth, which was nine times greater than the amount normally discharged, flow into the Buffalo River.*

Since 25 percent of the American population draws municipal water from wells and underground springs, the rising contamination of groundwater, particularly by household wastes from septic tanks, may eventually become a more serious problem than combined sanitary and storm sewerage. About 34 percent of our domestic wastes currently drains into septic systems, the oldest and generally least efficient means of treating sewage. After a few years the septic tanks frequently begin to fail and contaminate nearby streams and wells. To save the cost of constructing sewage systems, many housing developers in suburban areas during the post-war building boom installed thousands of septic tanks on small lots in highly impermeable soil. In many cases, clustered units soon saturated the ground, causing widespread seepage of toilet, kitchen, and laundry wastes. Even in communities where tap water does not froth

---

* U. S. Senate, "A Study of Pollution—Water," Staff report to the Committee on Public Works, 1963.

with a head of suds, septic systems may cause groundwater corruption by toxic materials that may not be detected for years or even decades.

While municipal waste disposal has risen more than 300 percent in this century, industrial pollution has increased more than 1,000 percent. Power plants contribute thermal wastes; slaughtering houses add offal and blood; food processing plants dispose of trimmings; mining operations pour acid into our streams; nuclear reactors and hospitals offer radioactive garbage; refineries season our waters with acids, alkalies, sulfides, ammonia, and phenols. Hundreds of additional waste products are discharged in the production and processing of canned goods, finished metal wares, chemicals, textiles, pulp, coke, pharmaceuticals, gas, and paper.*

Widespread use of new chemical compounds, particularly insect and weed killers, is creating a new and complex problem of great concern to many conservationists as well as medical experts and health officials. In 1943, there was only one synthetic organic insecticide on the market. Today, there are more than 200 basic chemicals available in thousands of different formulations. Liquids, dusts, and aerosols are being applied to homes, gardens, farm crops, and forests throughout the nation. Although most often applied to land for the control of insects and pests, the deadly potions frequently appear as run-off in treated areas and may be contaminating groundwater as well as streams and lakes. Many of these synthetic materials are extremely toxic to fish even in such low concentrations as less than one part per million parts of water. This was demonstrated by fish kills in 15 different streams of the Tennessee River Valley soon after the application of an insecticide to over 400,000 acres of cotton in eight Alabama counties.

Perhaps even more devastating to fish is the rising temperature of the country's lakes and streams due to the disposal of hot waste effluents. Thermal pollution is currently destroying the fishing grounds of trout, salmon, whitefish, and fresh water

---

* C. Fred Gurnham; *Industrial Wastewater Control,* Academic Press, New York and London, 1965.

Pigeon River pollution

North Carolina Wildlife Commission

herring by reducing the oxygen content of water. It takes only a small temperature rise in a stream to make it lethal to trout, and even though the slight increase occurs once a year for a mere two hours on a single day, the watercourse can lose its trout forever.

There are fewer harmful air pollutants than water contaminants but the number of individual sources is far greater. The air is fouled by the emissions of incinerators, factories, plants, refineries, space heaters in homes and buildings, and all motor vehicles—planes, trains, trucks, autos, lawn mowers, generators, etc. Wherever there is fire, indeed any form of combustion, there is pollution. Normally, of course, the air is seldom corrupted by an individual source in isolation, and critical air pollution problems are generally related to large numbers of emissions concentrated within an airshed.

The major harmful and damaging pollutants are carbon monoxide, carbon dioxide, hydrocarbons, fluorides, nitrogen oxides, sulfur oxides, acidic aerosols, and fine particles known as *particulate matter* in technical jargon. This may consist of soot, coal dust, fly ash, asphalt droplets, airborne soil and sand, metallic shavings, or any other powdered material generated during erosion, corrosion, construction, or the manufacture of industrial products.

Burning coal in the furnaces of homes and apartment buildings is often disregarded, but it can lead to a large concentration of pollutants in urban air. Upon combustion, bituminous coal, particularly, emits solids, oxides of nitrogen, sulfur, and various organic substances. Often sulfur dioxide is converted into sulfuric acid by oxygen and water vapor in the air or on the lining of your lungs. All these substances have been implicated in the growing magnitude of air pollution. Domestic incineration creates even filthier pollutants than space heating. Thousands of communities without adequate refuse collection force their citizens into the practice of open burning or incineration of paper, leaves, garbage, and refuse in their backyards. This can be a major source of the airborne organic matter and solids that are a bane to housewives and janitors. Even more

New York State Air Pollution Control Board

Bronx automobile burning

offensive is the vogue of open burning at city dumps, junkyards, and construction sites.

Municipalities frequently contribute to their air pollution problems by the operation of sewage plants, asphalt plants, incinerators, power plants, and public transportation systems which utilize fossil fuels. Both municipal and private incinerators can play a significant role because of the large number of uncontrolled emissions. Smoke, fly ash, and odors from such sources have been troublesome, especially with the increasing consumption of paper, plastics, and other synthetic materials prevalent in our affluent society.

The most common irritating and potentially toxic gas emitted by industrial operations is sulfur dioxide, formed during the combustion of coal and oil. Industries such as nonferrous metal, sulfuric acid, and wood pulp manufacturers, use sulfur dioxide in their operations and lose some of this gas while processing their materials. Another highly toxic pollutant is a group of fluoride dusts generated in sintering and open-hearth smelting, aluminum production, superphosphate manufacturing, and in making brick and tile.

In addition to the chemical and metallurgical manufacturers, there are two other significant categorical sources of industrial air pollutants. One of these consists of petroleum refineries which process 12 million barrels of crude oil each day. Refinery emissions include oxides of sulfur, particulate matter, hydrocarbons, oxides of nitrogen, ammonia, aldehydes, and organic acids. In addition to flue exhaust, pollution leakage can occur at hundreds, even thousands, of sources as every pump gland and pipe fitting is a possible, even if small, contaminator.

As the combustion of coal, petroleum, and gas generates about 80 percent of this nation's vast source of electrical energy, power plants play a prominent role in air pollution. Their towering stacks emit fly ash, carbon soot, and sulfur oxides in enormous quantities, as any Manhattan housewife should know. The production of sulfur oxides is common to the combustion of both petroleum and coal, and nitrogen oxides are emitted in the burning of all three fossil fuels used to produce electricity.

U.S. Public Health Service

Smokestacks smudging the city skyline

Ships, planes, trains, and trucks are contaminating factors in transportation pollution. These are relatively minor, however, when compared with the corruption of our atmosphere by autos. The magnitude is growing rapidly and in some areas automobile pollution is more serious than industrial contamination.

This would not be true if a gasoline engine could be designed to achieve complete combustion. An ideal engine would only generate water vapor and carbon dioxide. Neither by-product can be seen or smelled and both are nontoxic. Combustion, however, is never complete, and often it is highly inefficient. This is particularly evident in older cars that rattle down our roads trailing banks of blue and black fumes. Consequently, autos exhaust a host of hydrocarbons and various nitrogen oxides, prodigious amounts of carbon monoxide, sulfur compounds, aldehydes, organic acids, ammonia, and solids (including lead, zinc, metallic oxides, and carbon), in addition to carbon dioxide and water vapor. Although not all have been identified in the laboratory, chemists now know there are at least 200 compounds in auto emissions. The composition and quantity of these gases vary with the type of engine, motor condition, mode of operation, and the particular gasoline being consumed. It's quite clear that driving a car is a lot more complicated than filling the tank, turning the ignition key, and stepping on the accelerator. Obviously, every operating auto does a lot more than transport adults, children, luggage, and pets.

The dynamics and chemistry of polluted urban air become even more complex after emission. The interactions of the various contaminants are influenced not only by composition and concentration but also by factors such as solar radiation and humidity. This was revealed by the realization that on bright, sunny days over Los Angeles, unaccountably large concentrations of ozone accumulated in the atmosphere. Studies on ozone, nitrogen, hydrocarbons, and aldehydes led Professor Haagen-Smith of the California Institute of Technology to establish the generally accepted principles of photochemical smog formation. He found that the absorption of ultraviolet light by these gases produces relatively large concentrations of atomic oxygen which form ozone or react with organic pollutants to yield the compounds which cause eye irritation, crop damage, and low visibility. Ozone also seems to account for accelerated rubber cracking, while the oxidation of sulfur dioxide to sulfur trioxide forms sulfuric acid vapor.

Taken individually, the sources of air and water pollution do not account for the devastation from the massive assault on our environment and the crisis we face today. Some of these sources have existed for many years. In isolation, the relatively novel, lethal sources of contamination would rarely cause a public hazard. The character of air and water contamination, however, has been radically altered by the enormous rate of urbanization, industrialization, and transportation. When concentrated in a regional airshed or waterway, its magnitude—a consequence of gargantuan material demands and a colossal irresponsibility for our vital resources—can be catastrophic.

death by inversion

THE DISGUSTING sights and nauseating smells of pollution are the lesser evils of a massive inversion of our environment. Megatons of pollutants are a menace to our health and even to our lives, for contamination, sufficiently concentrated, can be a sudden and violent killer.

History is full of the accounts of plagues and epidemics that were spawned by infectious water contaminants. Cholera, typhus, and dysentery were scourges until the 20th century. Diphtheria is still another killer borne by ravaged water. As late as 1960—before the broad application of the Salk vaccine— the dreaded polio virus penetrated water treatment screens to take its toll of human life and strength.

With these exceptions, however, corrupted water has generally been recognized by its appearance, taste, or odor. In this way, fortunately, man is better off than he is in the case of polluted air, where he has neither an alternate supply nor a simple way of purification.

Aside from polio, there have been no recent epidemics of fatal diseases in America caused by polluted water. Their threat still lingers, but, in most cases, health officials have been able to recognize the danger in time to prevent catastrophies. This excellent record of hygienic water, however, may be an illusion attributable to medical ignorance about virus invasions—particularly those which cause cancer—and our indifference to ecology and the food chain that binds us to insects and to plankton in the sea. Today our waterways are suspect of contamination by insecticides, herbicides, pesticides, and other hazardous chemicals. These concoctions already are killing fish and poisoning oysters, and now there is growing concern about possibly lethal accumulations in human tissue or chronic effects and their eventual impact on our health.

Among the documented cases of wildlife mortality attributed to synthetic poisons in *Silent Spring*, Rachel Carson cites the death of Miramichi River salmon in New Brunswick, the effective elimination of the "swan grebe" at Clear Lake, California, and the mortality of cats and livestock in Sheldon, Illinois. The lethal effect of these industrial brews has not been limited to wildlife, for even humans who have handled man-made poisons have been victims in sudden and excruciating ways.

Certainly, the most damning evidence to the crime of massive water pollution, and possibly an indication of its menace to human life, is the 1964 report by the U. S. Public Health Service. In 40 states along 1,451 miles of streams and shorelines and 12,637 acres of lake water, it estimates that 18,400,000 fish were killed. About 15 percent consisted of game fish, and a total of 6,000,000 dead fish was classified as having some commercial value. The report cited industrial pollution as the major cause of death with a total of 12,700,000 fish. Municipal wastes were blamed for the death of 4,100,000 fish and toxic substances from agricultural operations for 1,500,000. The largest individual kill occurred near New Miami, Ohio, where industrial pollution destroyed an estimated 7,800,000 fish. The second largest incident, affecting some 2,000,000 fish, was caused by pollution from the municipal sewage system in Santa Barbara, California.

The most gargantuan—certainly the most evident—crime of corruption is the devastation of the Great Lakes. Ironically, they are dying of eutrophication, the aging of water, which is accelerating rapidly because of the enormous quantities of nitrogen and phosphorous-rich waste material being discharged in the lakes at this very moment.

Brownsville (Pa.) *Telegraph*

Dead fish in Ten Mile Creek

One of the visible signs of an aging lake is an overgrowth of weeds and algae, forming green scum which turns crystal waters into pea soup. Slimy, stinking masses pile up on beaches, clog water treatment filters, and destroy aquatic life. When teamed with industrial wastes and raw municipal sewage, they are a hazard to health. For this reason, beaches in New York, Ohio, Michigan, and Wisconsin have been closed. Even the lovely Chicago lakefront—still free of algae drifts—is now under close scrutiny by U.S. Public Health officials.

Lake Erie, the shallowest and most polluted of the five Great Lakes, is already in an aquatic coma. To live along its shores is to know the stink of slime, dead fish, and human excrement—the smell of death. Its once-prized fish catches—walleyes, blue pike, yellow perch, and whitefish—are past history. The U. S. catch of blue pike, for example, has dwindled from 20 million pounds in 1936 to one thousand in 1963.

The major contribution to this enormous contamination is made by industries pouring wastes into every major stream emptying into Lake Erie—the Detroit, Maumee, Sandusky, Black, Rocky, Cuyahoga and Buffalo rivers. Detroit alone pours 1.5 billion gallons of waste and sewage into its waterway each day. The bacterial count in the Cuyahoga, which flows through Akron and Cleveland for a double dosage of industrial garbage, has been measured at a rate four times the level expected in a stream of raw sewage. The stream is so clogged with debris, oil, and flammable chemicals that its waters have been labelled as a fire hazard! Mayor Chester Kowal, on a cruise up the Buffalo River, said "The stink was overpowering, unbelievable, and disgusting."

Thousands of lakeside residents get into the act by pouring raw sewage directly into Erie. Rich in phosphates, these wastes accelerate the growth of slime on the lake's bottom. Some 87 tons of phosphates are dumped into the water each day, and each pound has the capability of breeding 350 tons of algae slime. As these underwater plants absorb enormous quantities of oxygen, some 2,600 square miles at the center of the lake have become a dead sea. There, in the world's largest cesspool, marine life is practically nonexistent.

Since Pasteur and Koch established a direct relationship between disease and contaminated water late in the 19th century, we have been acutely aware that polluted water has been responsible for thousands of human deaths throughout history. A similar recognition of the lethal aspects of air pollution was not suspected until 1930, when 63 residents of the Meuse Valley in Belgium died suddenly within a few days. The incident provoked an extensive investigation by health officials, whose report established a direct link between corrupted air and human mortality.

Three elements were discovered in a tragic configuration that was destined to recur. In the first place, the fifteen-mile stretch between the towns of Huy and Seraing is the site of considerable industry that includes coke ovens, blast furnaces, steel mills, glass factories and zinc smelters as well as chemical ferti-

Waste flowing into Lake Erie

lizer and sulfuric acid plants. In addition, homes, railroads, and river steamships in the area also are heavy users of coal. Second, in this portion of the Meuse, the valley is particularly narrow and the river bluffs are quite steep. Finally, in December of that year, a stagnant mass of air associated with a high pressure system was accompanied by unusually thick fog and a thermal inversion. For seven days, gases, particulate matter, and vaporized liquid accumulated to form a thick industrial smog that soon reached noxious levels. After three days, children in school fell to the floor unconscious, workers doubled up in pain and lay prostrate from nausea and vomiting, and housewives found themselves so weak they could hardly do routine chores around their homes. When the air was finally cleared by a heavy rainfall, 63 persons were dead and about 6,000 had suffered illness.

The official investigation concluded that the aged were affected more frequently and severely than the young. It also indicated that the cause of death and illness probably was gas generated by burning coal in the presence of atmospheric water droplets and absorbed on the surface of suspended particles which then got into the tracheo-bronchial tract and lungs where it was hydrolyzed into acids that resulted in irritation and burning of the membrane linings.

The same report predicted that similar disasters would take place again. They did; and the next one occurred in the Monongahela Valley in our own country. The circumstances nearly duplicated those of the Meuse Valley catastrophe.

About 30 miles south of Pittsburgh, the three communities of Donora, Webster, and Carroll, with a total population of some 14,000, nestle along a horseshoe bend of the Monongahela River. At this point, the valley is surrounded on three sides by steep hills. On Tuesday, October 26, 1948, a thermal inversion, accompanied by fog, placed a meteorological lid over a riverfront lined by plants producing steel, wire, zinc, and sulfuric acid. By Thursday the citizens of Donora could barely see across the street, and on Friday some persons were afflicted by nausea. On Saturday, 17 residents died in a community where the normal death rate is two per week. After the smog was dispersed by rain on the following day, 20 persons were dead and some 6,000 residents were ill with such afflictions as excessive coughing, sore throat, chest constriction, difficult breathing, nausea, vomiting, and smarting eyes.

Neither the incidence nor severity of affliction, according to the official U. S. Public Health Service report, appeared to be influenced by sex, race, occupational status, length of residence in the area, or degree of physical activity at the time of the smog's onset. Autopsies performed on three of the persons who had died showed that there were indications of acute changes in the lungs characterized by capillary dilatation, hemorrhage, edema, purulent bronchitis, and bronchiolitis.

The most infamous killer smog assaulted London, England, in 1952. Like the Meuse and Donora episodes, this too was caused by a thermal inversion which trapped industrial and residential pollutants in a fog so thick that visibility was reduced to zero. Concerts and shows had to be stopped because curtains of smog screened stages from view. Autos, buses, trains, and even boats collided as accident rates rose drastically and thousands abandoned their cars, strewing the roads with vehicles which intensified traffic jams. Eventually all river traffic was called to a halt.

Illness began within 12 hours after the onset of the "black fog" on Thursday, December 4. Hospitals rapidly began to fill up as the number of emergency calls rose to about four times the normal amount. The first indication that the smog was lethal occurred at the Smithfield Club livestock show, one of England's most important farm exhibitions. Cows and bulls began panting heavily, grew feverish, and refused to eat. Their condition became so severe that a dozen animals were slaughtered. A thirteenth expired without further human interference. Examination of the carcasses showed that the creatures had suffered from extreme respiratory irritation, resulting in emphysema, pneumonia, and edema.

On Friday, the human death rate jumped 39 percent, causing 114 more deaths than usual. On Saturday, the number of deaths was 209 above normal, a 70 percent increase. The next day the death rate exploded to an increase of 602 deaths. On Monday, the day the smog was dispersed by wind and rain, there were still 618 more deaths than usual, and on a clear sunny Tuesday the mortality rate was still two and a half times higher than normal.

That week, health officials recorded an extra 2,851 deaths and, in the following week, an additional 1,224. Consequently, the mortality attributed to the 1952 killer smog is generally estimated to be 4,000 human beings. One medical expert, however, contends that the effects were felt for at least five weeks after the fog dissipated and resulted in the deaths of at least 6,000 persons. Another physician believes that victims of the smog died as long as twelve weeks after the event and that the smog directly contributed to the death of 8,000 humans.

The official British Government reports cautiously states:

> While the available evidence does not allow of a clear indict-
> ment of any one constituent of the fog, the conclusion is in-
> escapable that the excessive mortality and increased incidence
> of respiratory illness during and immediately after the fog of
> December 1952 were the result of irritation of the respiratory
> tract by contaminants of the fog. The irritants mainly respon-
> sible were probably those derived from the combustion of coal
> and its products and their lethal effects were wholly exer-
> cised in persons already suffering from chronic respiratory or
> cardiovascular disorders.

Less than a year after the London disaster, a thermal inversion trapped pollutants in the New York metropolitan area for
nine full days until smoke reached a level that was six times
greater than normal and the amount of sulfur dioxide in the air
rose to an unprecedented five times normal. High concentrations of fly ash, dust, soot, grit, and various other particles accumulated in the still air until a cubic mile of air was saturated
with three and a half tons of this urban garbage. Visibility was
so bad that both Kennedy and La Guardia airports were shut
down. Even ferry service to the Statue of Liberty was suspended. On the eleventh day, wind broke up the thermal inversion and rain cleansed the air of its accumulated filth. By then
more than 200 New Yorkers were dead as a direct consequence
of atmospheric toxicity. This morbid fact was not discovered,
however, until nine years later, when the death records of similar periods before and after the 10-day episode were compared.
The study, made by two New York medical experts, also revealed that in addition to the deaths, a significantly large
number of persons had suffered cardiac and respiratory distress
as a result of the smog.

The full effect of that smog will never be known. Adequate
data are lacking for Boston, Philadelphia, Baltimore, Atlanta,
Pittsburgh, Cleveland, Detroit, or for the hundreds of other
communities that were blanketed by the same pall that choked
New York City, to guess intelligently at a probable toll of human life!

In January 1956, London was again polluted by a thermal
inversion that resulted in the death of 1,000 persons on a single

day. Then in 1962, exactly ten years after the infamous black smog of 1952, the smoke concentration rose to twelve times its normal level, and the fog became so thick that the London airport was shut down. As a result of the lessons of the earlier tragedies, the Ministry of Health warned sufferers of heart and chest complaints to remain indoors. The Air Pollution Medical Research Unit also cautioned that babies and elderly persons should have the least possible exposure to the outdoor air. These precautions apparently saved many lives, for when the smog cleared after four days there were only 750 attributable deaths in its wake.

At the same time, a stagnant air mass over the northeastern United States caused a steady and alarming increase in pollution concentrations from Richmond to Boston. Sulfur dioxide levels in New York City and Philadelphia rose to five times normal. Solid airborne matter was measured from four to five times its normal level. Fortunately, the aerial sewage was soon blown out to sea. As Senator Ribicoff of Connecticut stated in Congress, "If we hadn't been lucky—if this mass of contaminated air hadn't been blown out over the ocean in time—the United States might have suffered the worst air pollution calamity in history." Just one year later, in 1963, during a 15-day bout of intense contamination, there were 404 excess deaths in New York City, according to a recent special study by a research group under the direction of Dr. Leonard Greenburg. An editorial in the New York World-Telegram and Sun* recently speculated:

> Dr. Greenburg's report on a 15-day period in 1963 is disturbing enough of itself. It is all the more so in raising questions it does not and cannot answer.
>
> How many other such periods have there been?
>
> How many "excess deaths" are caused, or precipitated, by polluted air in the average season or the average year?
>
> How much of what is accepted as the "normal" death rate is in reality excessive—caused or aggravated by air pollution?
>
> These are questions that beg desperately for research that will lead to not merely more accurate measurements but more effective antidotes and preventives.

* Copyright 1965 by the *New York World-Telegram and Sun.*

New York Journal American

New York and smog

Chapter 6

pollutants by the megaton

THE DEATHS of humans, livestock, game, fish, birds, plants, and lakes are not at all shocking when you consider the magnitude of environmental pollution in the United States. On the contrary, it is remarkable that there have not been many more disasters, and one cannot help but wonder how many more silent assaults and "excessive" deaths have occurred that went unrecognized. Such questions far outnumber their answers. We do know with certainty—derived from the studies of the Meuse, Donora, London, and New York disasters—that sufficient quantities and concentrations of air pollutants can contribute to human mortality. We also know that viruses and some of the newer chemicals often are not eliminated from drinking water by conventional treatment.

Furthermore, the staggering growth of synthetic organic compounds poses yet another alarming threat of corruption. In the last 25 years, the annual chemical production has risen almost 40 times, from 650,000 tons in 1940 to about 25 million tons in 1965. Detergent production alone has now reached two million tons per year. Since 20 parts of detergent to one million parts of water can be toxic to fish, this output has the potential for poisoning 100 billion tons of water and producing fantastic quantities of foam and scum. Many of the other new chemicals —as well as their precursors and byproducts—get into our waterways during their production. Others are flushed into

50

our lakes and streams by storm runoff and in waste disposal. The potential threat of pesticides, for example, is sufficiently terrifying to warrant a vigorous research effort now underway by government laboratories to determine their health effects in the minute quantities present in polluted waters.

Even this abundance of new chemicals, however, is minor compared to the quantities of waste materials generated by the nation's factories, canneries, refineries, mines, and power plants. In 1960, our industries used 160 billion gallons of water each day to produce goods and gadgets as well as wastes that amounted to the equivalent of the untreated sewage of 150 million persons, a tenfold increase in this century. In 1965 industrial wastes probably equaled the sewage of 190 million people. Without extensive remedial action, this figure will double within the next two decades. Rickles gives us an insight into the growing magnitude of industrial corruption by listing the percentage of plants in various industries that did not have waste treatment facilities in 1959.*

Industry	Percent Without Waste Treatment
Automobile	48
Beet Sugar	6
Coal Preparation	12
Corn and Wheat Milling	50
Distillery	62
Food Processing	27
Machinery	71
Meat	5
Natural Gas Compression	0
Photography	50
Poultry Processing	12
Pulp and Paper	32
Salt	87
Soap and Detergents	56
Sugar, Cane	52
Tanning, leather	38
Textiles	73

It should be pointed out that since 1959, many of these firms have initiated pollution control. Unfortunately, the pace of correction is far slower than the growth of industry, a contributing factor to the passage of the Water Quality Bill of 1965. This

* R. Rickles, *Pollution Control*, Noyes Development Corp., 1965.

was also reflected in President Johnson's comments when he
signed the act:

> No one has a right to use America's rivers and America's
> waterways, that belong to all the people, as a sewer. . . .
> There is no excuse for a river flowing red with blood from
> slaughterhouses. There is no excuse for paper mills pouring
> tons of sulphuric acid into the lakes and streams of the people
> of this country. There is no excuse . . . for chemical compa-
> nies and oil refineries using our major rivers as pipelines for
> the toxic wastes.

While industry is a frequent and convenient whipping boy
for the pollution of our waterways, it is only one of three major
sources of corruption. The one rarely mentioned is agriculture
although farmers use 150 billion gallons of water each day,
mostly for irrigation. A significant portion of this water is
absorbed by the soil or evaporated, but most of it washes salts,
alkalies, pesticides, herbicides, insecticides, and other agricultural chemicals into nearby waterways. Unlike industry, *none*
of these wastes gets any treatment at all. Some of our leading
water resource experts are now intensively researching this
problem with the objective of developing methods for reclaiming
some of the vast quantities of water that cannot now be reused
and that are devastating to rivers and streams.

The third major source—perhaps the most dangerous, certainly the most odious—gushes right out of our own homes. It is
both startling and ludicrous to note that in the Space Age only
one third of municipal sewage gets adequate treatment. The remaining two-thirds do not. In fact, 2,139 American communities flush raw sewage directly from the toilet to the nearest
stream or lake!

The Federal government itself—whose officials are striving
to awaken the American people to the dangers of pollution—
stands accused of being a significant contributor to water contamination. In the July 14, 1965, issue of *The Washington Post*,
columnist Drew Pearson cited some paradoxical cases of water
pollution by Federal facilities which were brought to light by
Representative Robert F. Jones of Alabama, a vigilant crusader
for clean waterways. While the President and his wife seek a

more beautiful nation and Congress responds by drafting legislation aimed at preventing gross pollution by industry and
municipalities, the Navy's Air Materiel Center in Philadelphia
dumps 83,400 gallons of sewage and 329,800 gallons of untreated industrial wastes into the Delaware River every day. On the
same day, its shipyard at Portsmouth, Virginia, discharges
800,000 gallons of industrial filth into the Elizabeth River. In
the Midwest, a Federal penitentiary at Terre Haute, Indiana,
daily pumps 200,000 gallons of criminal wastes through an inefficient treatment plant with a potential capacity of only half
that amount. Even more ironical are the government hospitals
at Charleston, South Carolina, and Alexandria, Louisana. One
discharges 250,000 gallons of untreated sewage into Charleston
harbor every day while the other contributes 111,000 gallons to
the flow of the Red River.

Today there is six times more pollution in our rivers,
streams, and lakes than 60 years ago, and the amount is increasing. The Hudson River alone carries over 600 million gallons of sewage and industrial wastes to the Atlantic each day—
219 billion gallons a year! Even Chicago, which has the most
modern sewage treatment facilities of any large city in America, is discharging effluents into the Illinois River equivalent to
the raw sewage of a million people daily.

Two hundred and fifty-two sewer outfalls discharge wastes
into three Milwaukee rivers. As a result, the city's four beaches
have been closed since 1959. The Detroit area dumps 20 million
pounds of contaminant materials into Lake Erie every day in
a waste flow totaling 1.6 billion gallons. Ten years ago in
the St. Louis metropolitan area, an Illinois-Missouri commission found that along the Mississippi River, there were 155
waste and storm outlets along 22 miles on the Missouri shore
and 45 along 29 miles of Illinois banks. The city of Memphis
dumps 60 million gallons of raw sewage every day into this
same river further downstream. Old Man River now carries
more sludge than mud.

An American-Canadian International Joint Commission has
determined that the flow of industrial pollutants from Lake Su-

perior into Lake Huron amounts to hundreds of millions of gallons a year. Six major plants in the dense industrial complex between Chicago, Gary, and Hammond discharge each day a billion gallons of waste that includes 50 tons of oil, 35,000 pounds of ammonia, 3,500 pounds of phenols and *3,000 pounds of cyanide!* These chemicals drain into the sluggish Calumet River and placid Wolf Lake, then flow into Lake Michigan where they exterminate aquatic life and degrade Chicago's splendid beaches.

While most water pollutants are carried away from our homes by sewers and away from cities and croplands by rivers to plague our downstream neighbors, the bulk of air pollutants hover about their sources to molest nearby property. Air pollution is particularly immediate and intimate to anyone who cleans the urban filth that settles in apartments, homes, and hotels. Dustfall is both the dirtiest and most prominent pollutant as well as the easiest to measure, as is now done in many cities. One of our grubbiest cities is New York, where the average fallout of solid material is about 60 tons per square mile each month. Commissioner Arthur J. Benline of the Department of Air Pollution has stated that 524,721,024 pounds of soot drifted down through the air in New York City in 1961. In Chicago's Loop, where many major offices and large department stores are located, as much as 120 tons of solid matter have fallen on a square mile within a single month.

To get an accurate idea of how much particulate matter is generated in an urban area, the Robert Taft Sanitary Engineering Center of the U.S. Public Health Service sampled air within a square mile up to a height of 100 feet in eleven cities across the nation. The results of this study indicate that the amounts of filth in these cities are as follows:

City	Tonnage	City	Tonnage
Detroit	153	Washington	58
Chicago	124	Houston	57
Los Angeles	118	San Francisco	46
New York	108	Pittsburgh	45
Philadelphia	83	Salt Lake City	24
Atlanta	61		

Chicago Tribune

Chicago and smog

The most extensive studies on total pollution in an individual city have been conducted in Los Angeles. Estimates by the Air Pollution Control District there indicate that for every 1,000 gallons of gasoline consumed, 3,000 pounds of carbon monoxide, 200 to 400 pounds of hydrocarbons and 50 to 150 pounds of nitrogen oxides are discharged into the atmosphere. The daily air pollution due only to motor vehicles in Los Angeles County came to about 10,500 tons in 1961. Most experts believe this is anywhere from one-half to two-thirds the amount of total emissions, which means not less than 15,000 tons of pollutants daily. Today that figure is probably somewhere between 20 and 30 thousand tons daily, or over seven million tons of carbon monoxide, carbon dioxide, hydrocarbons, nitrogen oxides, sulfur compounds, aldehydes, organic acids, ammonia, and solids each year.

The magnitude of automobile emissions is growing swiftly as the number of motor vehicles on our highways and streets is increasing twice as rapidly as the population. Over the past 20 years, there has been an average of more than 10 million additional vehicles on the road every fifth year. In 1942 there were 32 million registered motor vehicles. Today there are over 82 million, and by 1970 we are expected to have 103 million operating in the United States. Although Los Angeles has had the most severe automotive pollution problem in this country, it may soon be joined by other cities that now have more autos per square mile than Los Angeles with 1,350. As of 1962 Chicago had 1,541 automobiles per square mile, Detroit 1,580, New York 2,200, Philadelphia 3,730, Denver 3,951, and Washington, D.C. 4,100 passenger cars for each square mile.

The amount of air pollutants from any given source in any area varies considerably with the day of the week, weather, wind, season, and character of emitting sources. While autos seem to be responsible for over half of the air pollution in Los Angeles, for example, industry apparently is the source of about 85 percent of Louisville's atmospheric contamination. In New York City, the domestic heating of apartment buildings and incineration play important roles. Categorization of these sources by type and quantities cannot be measured accurately. For these reasons, Professor Rolf Eliassen of MIT developed a set of statistics in 1956 for a metropolitan area with 100,000 persons. His formulations are based on air studies in New York, Cincinnati, Louisville, Chicago, Portland, San Francisco, and Los Angeles. He concluded that the total metropolitan activities of 100,000 persons result in an average daily emission of 603,000 pounds of pollutants. Interestingly, over 50 percent (337,200 pounds) consists of solid particles, most of it from random sources such as open burning, incineration, construction, and various industrial operations. In the case of widespread coal and oil combustion, backyard incineration and open dump burning, domestic and municipal sources are estimated to contribute about 32 percent of the total emissions. Where heating is done primarily by gas and oil and large efficient incinerators are employed, this figure is reduced to a mere seven percent of metropolitan air pollution.

If Professor Eliassen's calculations are applied to 75 million persons living in 1,200 areas with major or moderate pollution problems, the total annual emissions come to 82 million tons. This may seem like a staggering amount of corruption, but actually it is a very modest and cautious estimate when compared with over 120 million tons of pollutants attributed to motor vehicle emissions alone in a report on "Motor Vehicles, Air Pollution, and Health" from the Surgeon General to the U. S. Congress in 1962. In addition to this pollution from 82 million registered vehicles, however, we should add the emissions of 300,000 industrial operations, millions of space heaters, thousands of incinerators and open fires, plus nearly 500 mountains of coal refuse burning uncontrollably—in Alabama, Alaska, Colorado, Illinois, Indiana, Kentucky, Montana, New Mexico, Ohio, Pennsylvania, Tennessee, Utah, Virginia, West Virginia, and Wyoming—to get an inkling of air corruption in the United States.

Besides particulate matter, our major air pollutants are carbon monoxide, oxides of sulfur, and oxides of nitrogen, all generated by the combustion of fossil fuels. In addition to the gaso-

line combustion emissions cited earlier, 1,000 gallons of fuel oil
are reported to produce 300 pounds of sulfur oxides and 16
pounds of other pollutants. A ton of coal generates 200 pounds
of solids and 48 pounds of sulfur and nitrogen oxides. Based on
1962 studies of annual energy and fuel requirements,* we estimate that in 1965 the American people consumed 70 billion gallons of motor fuel, four billion barrels of fuel oil, and 500 million tons of coal. Simple multiplication gives us the following
statistics on fossil fuel emissions.

Fossil Fuel	Consumption	Emissions
Motor Fuel	70 billion gallons	126 million tons
Fuel Oil	4 billion barrels	35 million tons
Coal	500 million tons	62 million tons
TOTAL		223 million tons

On the basis of metropolitan air pollution studies referred to
in Professor Eliassen's work, it seems reasonable to guess there
are at least an additional 40 million, perhaps as much as 75
million, tons of solid material from random nonfossil fuel
sources. In a word, human activity probably injected something
like 300 million tons of pollutants into the air over America in
1965. This is a staggering figure, but it is downright frighten-
ing to realize that one part of sulfur dioxide per million parts of
air will damage vegetation, and that gladioli have been injured
by concentrations of hydrogen fluoride as low as one part per 10
billion parts of air!

What, then, is the annual economic and health impact of a
multibillion-pound injection of gases and particles into our atmosphere together with a multitrillion-gallon ejection of infectious and poisonous wastes into our waterways?

---

* Report of the National Fuels and Energy Group to the Committee on Interior
and Insular Affairs, U. S. Senate, September, 1962.

Chapter 7

the multibillion dollar loss

ONCE UPON a time, the crystal waters of the Potomac were so full of fish that Captain John Smith reported they could be dipped out of the river effortlessly. Presidential families picnicked along its shores. Teddy Roosevelt frequently took a morning dip in the lovely river before taking on his White House chores. Six decades later, Arthur B. Hanson, vice chairman of the Coordinating Committee on the Potomac River Valley, angrily described the consequences of untreated sewage disposal along the entire length of the river. He told the Senate's Select Committee on National Water Resources in 1960 that the Potomac is "an open cesspool", that visitors to Washington "might reasonably expect to find a recreational mecca with fine bathing beaches, neat marinas, and wholesome fishing grounds. They find instead a natural sewage lagoon." At that time the Public Health Service reported that sewage was discharged into the North Branch of the Potomac from virtually all the towns and villages on the watershed and that sewage treatment was virtually nonexistent. In addition to this blight of one of our country's potentially finest recreational areas, sulfuric acid from the drainage of abandoned coal mines was found to be killing off plant and animal life and inhibiting the growth of bacteria which decompose organic garbage. The acid also damaged boats, bridges, dams, and other marine structures.

U.S. Public Health Service

Potomac River pollution

The formerly majestic Hudson, one of the world's most scenic rivers, was a fisherman's delight in the last century. Sturgeon could be found in its waters as far north as Albany. Today it is an open sewer that carries billions of gallons of human and industrial wastes to the sea. Instead of sturgeon, its waters host maggots and eels that feed on human excrement.

As early as 1917, according to a report by the New Jersey Board of Shell Fisheries, the world-famous seed oyster beds in Raritan Bay (between Staten Island and Sandy Hook) had been depleted because of "the flow of trade waste into the streams, sounds and bays of that locality." The same thing is happening to Chesapeake Bay where recently oyster beds have been declared hazardous to human health. This profitable industry now faces the danger of extinction along the Chesapeake shores of Virginia and Maryland.

In 1963, an estimated five million fresh and salt water fish were killed in the Mississippi River by poisoning by pesticides and industrial wastes. Large areas of the Providence River, as well as Narragansett Bay have been closed because of the danger of infectious diseases. The Delaware is heavily contaminated by sewage and industrial wastes as it stinks its way through Philadelphia. Below Atlanta, the Chattahoochee is too polluted for swimming, as are areas on the Atlantic between Savannah and Brunswick where oysters unfit to eat have been identified as a source of hepatitis. The Columbia River is contaminated with radioactive wastes of nuclear reactors at Hanford, Washington. There have been fish kills in the Red River and the San Joaquin. Indeed, what river system in America is not contaminated? The Mohawk? The Connecticut? The Missouri? The Ohio? The Snake? The Rio Grande? Who can say what the toll has been to fish, wildlife, beauty, tourism, and the depreciation of property values?

Instead of providing prized "riparian rights," private bathing beaches, boating facilities, and majestic scenery, these waterways are now often foul with stench, disgusting panoramas, and the danger of diseases. Initially expensive and desirable home sites have fallen in value and are difficult to sell at any price. This economic loss to home owners is paralleled by financial disaster to commercial enterprises in recreational tourism.

We cannot measure such economic and esthetic losses, but we can get an inkling of their magnitude by examining the rising costs to municipalities supplying water for household use. At the beginning of the century water could be used directly as it came from clean streams. Distribution cost a nominal eight to ten cents per thousand gallons. Most often, the homeowner did not pay any fee for his water since he had an abundant, uncontaminated supply from the well in his backyard. As our cities became more heavily industrialized, these sources vanished, and it became necessary to purify water before its distribution. Construction costs of treatment plants, financed with funds from bond issues, have increased property taxes considerably. The actual cost of purification itself has often risen to 20 or 30 cents per thousand gallons. This expense is passed on to consumers through taxes or water bills. As our water supplies become more and more contaminated by wastes and sewage, the cost of purifying water for personal and industrial use rises. In many localities contamination is so gross that it is no longer economically feasible or desirable to even attempt to treat water that is found in the city limits or nearby. Instead, alternate sources of supply are sought, sometimes hundreds of miles from the user's tap. Already many Americans feel the economic pinch, and during the past decade this sudden shrinkage of water supply has suddenly become a matter of considerable concern to millions who once took pure water for granted much as they still take clean air for granted.

Today, some 30 billion gallons of water are treated daily for municipal use. If man-made pollution in this water adds just one cent to the treatment costs of 1,000 gallons of water, it drives the national water bill up $118 million in a single year. An average increase of five to ten cents (annual cost of $590 million to over one billion dollars) is probably more realistic, and we may be dealing with an excessive water purification cost due to contamination of several billion dollars during the past decade. If one speculates about the pollution-inflated cost of water for industry and agriculture, which use nine times as much water as municipalities, we're obviously dealing with many billions of dollars of excessive costs in this century. This should be a horrifying speculation to profit-conscious industrialists and economists.

The most dramatic example of water contamination is the problem of detergents which form stable masses of foam many yards broad and long and many feet thick. In addition to being dangerous to navigation, such banks of foam have created safety

Altoona (Pa.) *Mirror*

Foam at the Altoona treatment plant

hazards by coating the decks of barges with slick films. Even swimmers have suffocated in these foamy drifts.

In contrast to soap, made from organic fats, currently used detergents are synthetic cleansing agents that resist decomposition by bacteria and often pass through extremely fine filtering systems. They are capable of extracting infectious bacteria, meaning that foam can be a carrier of epidemics. While synthetic detergents do not show harmful effects on human beings in amounts that are generally encountered, they are very poisonous to fish, and even small amounts will destroy marine life by interfering with oxygen absorption. Detergents can also slow down the process by which water is naturally purified. The presence of phosphorous has led to excessive growth of algae, as happened to Lake Nantua in France, once a paradise for vacationers who were drawn to its famous clear blue water. Today, it is a sickly yellow body of water attracting few tourists.

Although the synthetic cleansers are seldom found in the drinking water of large communities, they interfere with normal treatment and purification processes and significantly increase the cost of clean water. They are also a great nuisance in suburban homes serviced by wells and septic tanks. Surveys by health officials on Long Island in Suffolk County indicated that over 30 percent of the wells sampled were polluted with detergents. In the Minneapolis area, in another survey, half of some 54,000 private wells were found to be contaminated by cleansing agents. Similar conditions have been discovered in eleven other states.

A highly serious water pollution problem is caused by silt. Unlike the other pollutants, it is not a direct product of human activity. Man's ignorance and carelessness in cultivating the land and clearing forests, however, have contributed to a large increase in the volume of silt that is carried to the sea. Despite the expenditure of vast sums and tremendous effort, mountains of topsoil still pollute water systems, destroy aquatic life, clog dams, and foul water-processing plants. Silting, of course, can never be eliminated entirely, and even a significant reduction will require improved agricultural practices and reforestation programs for many years.

Pollution by municipal sewage and industrial wastes, on the other hand, can be reduced or eliminated in any community within months. While the laws regarding drinking water are strictly enforced in every state, harmful bacteria infest and proliferate in thousands of streams and rivers carrying billions of gallons of sewage. It is incredible that in a modern, wealthy country, an estimated 3,000 communities in the United States do not have adequate sewage treatment plants and that over 2,000 do not have any sewage facilities at all! This is matched by 25,000 companies, representing all major industries, which are still discharging untreated manufacturing wastes directly into our waterways. Congressman Peter Rodino of New Jersey pungently sized up the situation during a speech in the House of Representatives:

> We can sum up what is happening to the streams through-out our country in just two words: America's shame. Water pollution in the United States has become a menace to our health and an economic problem which robs us of the water we need. It destroys fish and wildlife, threatens outdoor recreation areas, and is often an esthetic horror.

While we can only guess at the hidden costs of water contamination, there are numerous studies of the direct economic assault of air pollution on property, livestock and crops. Experts at the Department of Health, Education and Welfare believe that the total average cost per person in this country is $65 annually. This comes to over $11 billion per year. There are both higher and lower estimates, but all are conservative at best, and obsolete at worst.

Let us consider first some indirect and tenuous costs before focusing on studies of known losses directly attributed to air pollutants. The U. S. Weather Bureau indicates that urban areas lose 15 to 20 percent of the available sunlight because of decreased visibility caused by airborne dust, smoke, and other gaseous pollutants. It is logical and reasonable to assume that this is reflected in our electric light bills. Furthermore, urban areas have 30 percent more fog in the summer and 100 percent more fog in the winter than do rural areas. Urban areas also have five to ten percent more cloudiness and rain than in the country. Such conditions undoubtedly increase the hazards in auto traffic and cause delays in the landings and departures of airplanes. Decreased visibility due to smoke and haze alone, according to a Civil Aeronautics Board study of air crashes, was the cause of 15 to 20 of these accidents in 1962.

The harmful effects of air pollution on vegetation can be even more dramatic, and certainly suggest how it may be affecting urban children. Along many highways, especially in California, plants will not grow within several feet of the road because of automobile exhausts. Ozone, a product of automotive photochemical smog, is now considered to be the cause of emergence tipburn, a blight of eastern white pine. Agricultural researchers have also discovered that ozone causes lesions on grape leaves and damages such plants as spinach, alfalfa, rye, barley, parsley, and carnations. Tobacco, ironically, is among the most sensitive plants. For many years it has been subject to "weather" flecking, once thought to be a natural phenomenon that lowers the grade of leaves and makes them useless as cigar wrappers. In cases along the eastern seaboard, flecking has ruined tobacco crops overnight. In 1959, experimentalists established that the injury was caused by ozone in photochemical smog.

Sulfur dioxide, the most harmful pollutant of oil and coal combustion, kills cotton. Wheat and barley are sensitive to both ozone and sulfur dioxide. Oats die on brief exposure to either sulfur dioxide or photochemical smog. In the case of alfalfa, air pollution reduces the protein content of the crop.

Statistics from California to Florida translate these ravages into hard financial facts. The once flourishing flower industry in the Los Angeles basin grossed as much as $14 million in a single year. The most recent figures show this has been reduced to $4 million, and the decline continues as the metropolitan area expands. The orchid business in California has virtually been wiped out. On a single day in 1960, one siege of smog destroyed a lettuce crop worth $22,000. The citrus industry has also been hit hard. According to recent estimates, auto pollutants ruin

Effect of air pollution on an endive plant (left)

about $10 million worth of crops every year in Southern California alone.

Is Southern California unique? Not according to the Florida citrus growers in Polk County who abandoned 25,000 acres of orchards because of the fluoride emissions of phosphate factories. Not according to growers of apricots, grapes, blueberries, plums, peaches, strawberries, raspberries, and apples in 22 states across the nation where crop damage by automotive pollution has been identified.

Airborne fluorides are destructive to livestock as well as plant life. In one place in the state of Washington where aluminum factories have gone into operation, the number of local dairy cattle were reduced from 2,000 cows to 75. A head count of beef cattle in Polk County, Florida, indicated that the herds around the phosphate plants there had been reduced by 30,000 steers. An inspection of almost 800 cattle revealed that 71 percent had spongy teeth, thickened bones, and stiffening joints—the symptoms of fluorosis. One prize Brahma bull, purchased for $10,000 was sold for $36. There are similar records of fluoride poisoning in the Salt Lake Basin, in Tennessee's Blound and Maury counties, in the Los Angeles basin, and in both the Columbia and Spokane river basins.

What is the air pollution bill for farmers and ranchers? Experts at Health, Education and Welfare believe the annual damage to crops and livestock amounts to $500 million. If that figure is as cautious as their estimate of the total financial loss caused by air pollutants, agriculturalists may be sacrificing a full billion dollars every year for this kind of progress and prosperity.

The silent assault is even more devastating in our urban areas than it is down on the farm. A survey of 15 large cities, for example, indicated that the management of department stores estimated the annual losses due to air pollution in each operation varied from $20,000 to $50,000. Office building managers placed their losses between $11,000 and $35,000. Hospital executives thought their yearly air pollution bills ran between $4,000 and $20,000; hotel managers reckoned between $9,000 and $25,000. These costs related to cleaning, maintenance, and repairs made necessary by air pollution. The estimates seem to be supported by the St. Louis Hotel Association which reckons that the annual reduction in the cost of cleaning and redecorating as a result of a smoke abatement program in that city amounts to $153,880.

Corrosion, particularly in large manufacturing operations, is probably the most damaging air pollution action in the nation. It costs us many hundreds of millions, possibly billions, of dollars each year. Comparative studies of corrosion costs in urban and rural areas are highly enlightening. In Springfield, Illinois, a research group found that steel surfaces corroded thirty times faster in the city than in nearby rural areas. A similar study was made in Pennsylvania comparing the corrosion rates in a nonindustrial and an industrial community—State College and Altoona. In Altoona the increased rate of corrosion for nickel was 25 times faster than in State College. For zinc, it was 6 times greater; for brass 4.2; and for copper 3.2 times as fast.

Sulfur dioxide, the most important of the corrosive gases, combines with oxygen to form sulfur trioxide. This compound then reacts with water vapor to produce sulfuric acid. Principal oxidizing agents that cause corrosion are ozone, nitric oxide, nitrogen dioxide, and peroxides. All of these are the products of coal, oil, and gasoline combustion. Other damaging aerial acids include hydrogen sulfide, hydrochloric acid, nitric acid, and a number of tarry acids.

Metals like zinc and aluminum, normally considered resistant to acidic corrosion, are attacked by salts as well as by alkalies, which are emitted during the production of soap, glass, textiles, paper, ceramic materials, and chemicals. In addition to being encountered in marine atmospheres, corrosive salts such as ammonium sulfate and ammonium chloride are emitted in galvanizing, tinning, and soldering metals as well as in the manufacture of pharmaceuticals, fertilizers, and dyes.

Sulfur oxides attack limestone, marble, roofing, slate, mortar, and concrete. Rubber is destroyed by ozone and other oxidizing pollutants which also cause textile colors to fade and can even change the color of a dye. A somewhat ludicrous effect of nitrogen dioxide was an epidemic of nylon stocking runs in New York City. A more provocative incident occurred in Jacksonville, Florida, when sulfur dioxide partially undressed women wearing nylon blouses.

Air pollution is also hastening the deterioration of the World's stone art. In the April 13, 1964, issue of *The New York Times*, Milton Esterow reported that the Coliseum, the Arch of Titus and many frescoes in Rome have been damaged recently. "In Florence, the situation is described as disastrous. In West Germany, the state of North Rhine-Westphalia is spending $4 million annually to preserve disintegrating monuments."

Seymour Lewin, fine-arts professor at NYU's Institute of Fine Arts, said, "The rate of decay has increased greatly. The situation is getting more serious all the time. It's at its worst in

Cleaning off the residue from air pollution

highly industrialized cities. Many buildings have noticeably deteriorated in the last 20 years."

Currently, prized art work is being taken in from the outdoors all over Europe and in the United States. The only alternative is to wash statuary frequently with water. Scrubbing a statue is one thing; cleaning a building, such as Trinity Church in New York City, however, would cost fifteen to twenty thousand dollars. A skyscraper would run into hundreds of thousands of dollars.

What is the cost of urban corruption? Experts at HEW and PHS use the figure of $65 per person per year—$11 billion annually—for air pollution alone. According to Irving Michelson and Boris Tourin of the Environmental Health and Safety Research Association, this may be an extrapolated figure from studies of Pittsburgh in 1913. Recently they published a pilot study (shown in the accompanying table) confined to only a modest segment of household costs due to air pollution. In this study two homogeneous communities in the upper Ohio Valley—relatively clean Uniontown, and Steubenville with a severe pollution problem—were compared for the *differential* cost of interior and exterior maintenance, care of clothing, and personal care of hair and face. The cost analyses of the study distinguished between families with incomes under and over $8,000 a year, between home and apartment residences, and between self-maintenance and serviced maintenance. In families that averaged four persons per household, annual additional *out-of-pocket* costs for Steubenville households varied from $47 to $829. On a per capita basis self-maintenance groups averaged $29 more, while serviced households averaged $84, an average figure of $56 more for only personal care and property maintenance. If applied to the 75 million Americans living in urban areas with moderate or serious air contamination problems, the annual national bill comes to $4.2 billion in 1960, probably over $5 billion in 1965. This cost excludes deterioration of private, public, or industrial property and equipment, agricultural losses, the maintenance costs of nonresidential property and buildings, and completely ignores medical expenses, which could easily raise this figure by a multiple of two to four.

What is air pollution costing residents, business, and industries in New York City, Boston, Philadelphia, Baltimore, Atlanta, Cleveland, Cincinnati, Chicago, Detroit, Milwaukee, Minneapolis, Seattle, San Francisco, Los Angeles, Phoenix, Denver, Kansas City, Dallas, Houston, New Orleans, and Mobile? Were agricultural losses only $500 million in 1965? Is it unreasonable to hazard that the nation's annual air pollution bill alone amounted to $20 billion last year? And what was the cost of water pollution?

Like the question of excessive deaths, these questions of excessive costs are in desperate need of reliable answers.

SUMMARY TABLE

Increased Annual Dollar Costs in Downtown Steubenville Compared to Uniontown, for 28 activities, 1960

	income group*	Per Family		For the Community**		Per Capita,	
		Do-it-Yourself	Non-Do-it Yourself	Do-it-Yourself	Non-Do-it Yourself	Do-it-Yourself	Non-Do-It Yourself
Inside Maintenance	(1)	29	162	28,490	180,325		
	(2)	44	227	9,440	57,400		
Outside Maintenance	(1)	21	49	18,385	49,835		
	(2)	337	368	72,170	79,420		
Laundry and Cleaning	(1)	27	79	41,145	110,975		
	(2)	129	186	34,440	49,230		
Hair and Facial Care		9	48	5,950	74,170		
TOTALS				210,020	601,355	29	84
TOTALS, per family in private homes	(1)	86	338				
	(2)	519	829				
in apartments (No inside painting or decorating, no outside maintenance)	(1)	47	263				
	(2)	158	423				

*(1) Annual income under $8,000.
(2) Annual income $8,000 or more.

**Adjusted for the total number of families residing in downtown Steubenville (one eighth of their respondents did not state their family income).

Reprinted by permission from Irving Michelson and Boris Tourin, Environmental Health and Safety Research Association.

Chapter 8

black lungs, yellow eyes

"THE FACTS are in. Now is the time for action." That is Senator Abraham Ribicoff's reaction to the growing magnitude of air pollution and the mounting evidence of statistical studies, laboratory experiments, and expert medical opinion relating atmospheric corruption to respiratory diseases.

By contrast, opponents of increased Federal jurisdiction are reluctant to take any kind of action before cheaper abatement equipment is available. Champions of local and regional autonomy stress that costly mistakes may be made prior to a complete etiological understanding of pulmonary diseases. (Webster's International Dictionary defines *etiology* as the science or study of "all the factors that contribute to the occurrence of a disease or abnormal condition.") If this attitude were reflected in the Hippocratic oath, medical practice would have been moribund throughout history, and few, if any, patients would have received any treatment at all. Fortunately, lack of medical knowledge "beyond the shadow of a doubt" has rarely immobilized physicians.

In response to intellectual hairsplitting about etiology, a panel of medical experts at the 1962 National Conference on Air Pollution concluded: "It would be a mistake to leave this conference with the impression that there is insufficient evidence for action—now. The evidence that air pollution contributes to the pathogenesis of chronic respiratory disease is overwhelming." Another competent source, the staff report on air pollution to the U. S. Senate Committee on Public Works, states: "There is strong evidence that air pollution is associated with a number of respiratory ailments. These include (1) nonspecific infectious upper respiratory disease, (2) chronic bronchitis, (3) chronic constrictive ventilatory disease, (4) pulmonary emphsema, (5) bronchial asthma, and (6) lung cancer."

These conclusions reflect an alarming increase in respiratory disease as the country becomes more intensely urbanized and industrialized. At the beginning of the century, mortality due to emphysema was less than one death per 100,000. By 1950 the rate had doubled, and in the following decade it rose from 1.5 to 8 deaths per 100,000. Today, according to the records of the Social Security Administration, emphysema is the second leading cause of disability among workers 50 years and older. Only arteriosclerotic heart disease is more devastating. Meanwhile, as U. S. Surgeon General Luther L. Terry pointed out in his report to Congress in June, 1962, the mortality rate of lung cancer in this century has increased thirty times. That year, cancers of the respiratory system caused the death of 60,000 humans; emphysema and bronchitis accounted for another 16,000 deaths.

In a paper entitled, "Chronic Respiratory Diseases; A Mushrooming Challenge," Claire F. Ryder (Associate Chief for Care Services, U. S. Public Health Service) states: "In addition to being the major cause of death, chronic respiratory diseases were also certified as the underlying causes of 27,000 deaths in 1962 and were contributory to an additional 43,000 deaths that year." Although these figures are striking, other competent investigators believe that they understate the true situation and represent only "the visible portion of the iceberg". This opinion is supported by a National Health Survey of the United States in 1960. That year there were 11,717,000 persons afflicted by asthma and hay fever, 1,913,000 with chronic bronchitis, and 2,174,000 individuals with all other types of *chronic* respiratory conditions excluding sinusitis. The number of *acute* respiratory conditions—colds, bouts of flu, pneumonia, etc.—totaled 196,276,000.

In two years alone, from 1961 to 1963, deaths due to bronchitis in the United States rose 35 percent. This disease is far worse in Britain—birthplace of the Industrial Revolution—than anywhere in the world and causes the death of five times the number of persons killed by vehicles on British roads. The October 24, 1965, issue of *The London Observer* stated that "Smoky industrial cities like Warrington have a bronchitis death rate six times higher than a seaside town like Hastings. This disease costs 20 million pounds a year to treat and causes 30 million lost working days annually—the equivalent of 100 million pounds in wages and output."

When one considers the tons of filth in urban air and the delicacy of the human breathing apparatus, it is remarkable that the current assault on our beleaguered lungs is not even more devastating. Inhaled air is drawn down the bronchial tubes into nearly a billion microscopic sacs called alveoli. As Dr. Franklin Yoder, Director of Public Health in Illinois, points out, if it were possible to spread them out on a flat surface, the alveoli of two human lungs would cover a tennis court. The delicate sac appears to be the most vulnerable exposed structure of the human body. Despite the defensive mechanisms of cilia—minute, hairlike structures that line the respiratory tract—and mucous which filters foreign matter from the air we breathe, the lungs of urban residents eventually become coated with the grime, grit, and grease housewives wipe off their window sills daily. In the lung dissection of cadavers, consequently, pathologists can recognize long-time urban residents immediately. *The lining of the lungs is black.* Even among extremely heavy cigarette smokers, this condition is not duplicated in the lungs of rural residents.

One of the most significant facts emerging from the medical studies of environmental contamination is that chronic diseases are insidious and the causative mechanisms so subtle that many years may pass before a direct cause and effect relationship can be established. In fact, some experts suspect that a classical etiological approach will never establish simple direct relationships in individuals. Other analytical techniques to study highly complex and dynamic phenomena are required. One of these is known as *epidemiology*. It concentrates on studies of populations rather than on individual cases of a disease. It is particularly useful in studying insidious and delayed effects of harmful agents.

The first aim of the epidemiologist is to verify or disprove whether a disease may be related to an environmental factor. If there seems to be a connection between the prevalence of a disease and a certain group of persons, then the task is to ascertain the environmental circumstances that are associated with cause or aggravation of ill health. If a relationship can be statistically established, it serves to indicate areas for experimental biological efforts.

Epidemiological studies in the United States, England and Japan have shown that air pollution aggravates asthma. Studies in various English cities have established a relationship between air pollution intensity and mortality rates of chronic bronchitis. We now know that lung cancer occurs with higher frequency in cities than it does in rural areas where normally there is relatively little air pollution.

After reviewing some thirteen epidemiological studies at the 1958 National Conference on Air Pollution, Dr. Thomas F. Mancuso concluded that the evidence of an urban factor for lung cancer distinct from smoking patterns or questions of classification or diagnosis, seems to be secure. He cited his own study in Ohio which indicated that lung cancer mortality among native American males was twice as high in urban areas as in rural areas. In addition, even though the white males in urban areas smoked twice as much as nonwhite males, lung cancer incidence among nonwhites—who more often live in slum areas close to major sources of industrial pollution—was greater.

Even more significant is David Eastcott's study of English immigrants to New Zealand. For those over thirty, among both men and women, lung cancer mortality was 75 percent greater among the immigrants than among the natives, even though both groups were from similar ethnic backgrounds and had comparable smoking habits. In a group of English urbanites who immigrated to South Africa, the mortality of lung cancer was higher among the immigrants than among South Africans who smoke even more than the British. Among Norwegian emigrants who came to the United States, medical experts discovered that lung cancer developed at a rate midway between those who remained in Norway and the native Americans of Norwegian descent. To eliminate the complication of cigarettes, a study conducted in the British Isles focused on nonsmokers only. With tobacco completely excluded, lung cancer incidence in English cities was found to be *nine times* greater than in rural areas.

One of the most vigorous and conclusive epidemiological investigations was undertaken by a team of medical experts headed by the late Dr. Louis D. Zeidberg of Vanderbilt University. This group used some 38,000 data processing cards provided by the Tennessee Health Department. The cards contained information on people who had died in and near Nashville. Dr. Zeidberg's study showed that pollution consisting of smoke, haze, and sulfate particles could be directly related to deaths caused by influenza, pneumonia, tuberculosis, and various other respiratory diseases. Furthermore, there also was a correlation between air pollution levels and the incidence of deaths caused by hypertensive heart diseases, myocardial degeneration, and general arteriosclerosis.

These population studies are backed by experimental research in laboratories throughout the world. As Dr. Paul Kotin,* a noted pathologist, has pointed out,

> In relation to the carcinogenic hazards of air pollution, it is our belief that animal data are particularly pertinent. This is so for several reasons. First, in the panorama of lung cancer, all available evidence points to a dominant etiological role for exogenous agents present in our respiratory environment. These can be tested under controlled laboratory circumstances. With full knowledge that cancer rarely develops

---

*"Experimental Tumor Production With Air Pollutants", by Dr. Paul Kotin, *Proceeedings of the National Conference on Air Pollution*, U.S. Department of Health, Education and Welfare, Public Health Service, Washington, 1958.

subsequent to the action of a single factor, atmospheric pollution, both epidemiologically and in the laboratory, must be regarded as one of multiple factors operating in combination to result in lung cancer.

Laboratory analyses have identified 32 polynuclear aromatic hydrocarbons—including benzopyrene—in automobile exhaust alone. Some typical concentrations of benzopyrene are given in Table 1. Of these, nine are now known to be carcinogenic—cancer forming. The compounds have produced skin cancers and subcutaneous sarcomas (fleshy growths beneath the skin) by painting and injection. Particulate matter, such as carbon which blackens the lungs of urban dwellers, has been proven to be cancer producing. This is to be expected as English chimney sweeps have long been known to have an extremely high rate of lung and scrotum cancer. Inorganic elements that contribute to occupational cancers have been discovered in polluted air. They include arsenic, lead, beryllium, calcium, iron, and germanium. It has also been demonstrated that aldehydes and organic acids, though in themselves noncarcinogenic, interfere with the normal flow of the mucous stream that serves to prevent the accumulation of deposited material in the lungs. Another harmful effect of combustion has been established in connection with interference in the transport of oxygen by the red pigment of the blood. This is due to carbon monoxide which can seriously affect certain individuals who already have borderline effectiveness of the heart, lungs, or blood vessels.

In our own laboratories at IIT Research Institute, a scientific team led by Dr. Richard Ehrlich found that mice are far more susceptible to pneumonia infection when exposed to ozone, a constituent of the photochemical smog prevalent in Los Angeles. Similar results were obtained when the mice were exposed to nitrogen dioxide, a common automobile exhaust constituent. Ehrlich's group in an earlier experiment demonstrated that high concentrations of ozone led to edema and hyperemia.

In the Soviet Union, the Russians found that a single exposure of ozone and sulfuric acid (both of which are present in smog formed from exhaust gases) caused a 70 to 90 percent mice fatality, much greater than when either of these two pollu-

TABLE I

BENZOPYRENE CONCENTRATION IN AMERICAN CITIES

Air in 94 urban and 28 nonurban sites was sampled from January through March 1959.* The highest concentration found in a nonurban site was 51 micrograms of benzopyrene per gram of suspended particulate matter; 16 sampling sites had less than 10. Samples from nine of the urban sites had less than 10, and the others showed concentrations ranging up to 410. The 22 cities with concentrations greater than 100 are shown below.

City	Micrograms benzopyrene per gram suspended particulate matter
1. Richmond, Virginia	410
2. Montgomery, Alabama	340
3. Charlotte, North Carolina	290
4. Hammond, Indiana	280
5. Altoona, Pennsylvania	280
6. Knoxville, Tennessee	210
7. St. Louis, Missouri	200
8. Youngstown Ohio	190
9. Raleigh, North Carolina	180
10. Portland, Maine	180
11. Roanoke, Virginia	160
12. Des Moines, Iowa	160
13. Wheeling, West Virginia	140
14. Tampa, Florida	140
15. Flint, Michigan	140
16. Indianapolis, Indiana	120
17. Columbia, South Carolina	120
18. Chattanooga, Tennessee	120
19. Orlando, Florida	110
20. Dearborn, Michigan	110
21. Duluth, Minnesota	110
22. Cleveland, Ohio	110

* E. Sawicki, W. C. Elbert, T. R. Hauser, F. T. Fox, and T. W. Stanley, "Benzo(a)pyrene Content of the Air of American Communities." *Am. Ind. Hyg. Assoc. J.*, 21:443 (1960).

tants were used alone in the same concentrations. Significantly, pneumonia foci and edema were found in the lungs of the mice and plethora was observed in other organs including the brain.

Furthermore, without understanding the etiology of lung disease, physicians attributed one million six hundred thousand cases of illness to air pollution according to a survey published in the February, 1963 issue of *New Medical Materia*. Seventy-eight percent of the doctors blamed auto, truck, and bus exhaust; 66 percent blamed industrial operations; 37 percent blamed the incineration of garbage. Of the air pollution illnesses cited by the medical journal, 75 out of every 100 patients suffered from coughing, 71 from eye smarting, 61 from tearing, 52 from nasal discharge, 45 from dyspnea, 42 from sore throat and chest constriction, 41 from headache, 34 from choking, and 18 from nausea.

As long ago as 1956, the Los Angeles Medical Association revealed that 82 percent of its 1,500 member physicians were of the opinion that smog was a contributory factor in cancer of the lungs and air passages. Fifty-two percent of the doctors, incidentally, reported they knew of individuals who had left the area because of air pollution. In fact, 41 percent—some 600 doctors—actually advised one or more of their patients to leave the Los Angeles area for reasons of health. Another survey by the same association four years later revealed that by 1960 doctors had advised 10,000 patients to relocate in less polluted regions, and nearly one-third of the medical men and women polled admitted that they themselves had considered leaving Los Angeles because of their concern about the health effects of atmospheric contamination.

In view of the rapid growth of both population and air pollution, a thirtyfold rise in the mortality due to lung cancer—currently taking the lives of 40,000 Americans each year—is not surprising. In fact, it is incredibly low, and is a comment on the remarkable adaptability of the human body. As Dr. Yoder expressed it,

> One can fully appreciate the marvelous resourcefulness of the human body and its systems of defenses to maintain each body function within normal limits by warding off or neutralizing deleterious factors, whether they are biological, chemical or radiological. But there is a limit to the body's defenses. There is a limit to the amount of pollution that can be allowed to go into our surrounding sea of air . . . and man still survive.
>
> We must make it possible for man to breathe air that is substantially the same quality as the atmosphere supplied for

us by the natural phenomena of this third planet of our solar system. Since man himself is the pollutor, we must take whatever action is necessary in air pollution control programs (utilizing such emergency measures as required) to prevent the insidious varieties of disease and life-shortening chronic illnesses that occur through insults to our respiratory system, via polluted atmosphere.

A century ago, man knew less about water-borne disease than we now know about air-borne infections. Until the middle of the last century, most infections were explained by vapors or miasmas and often were treated by draining blood from a diseased body. In the wake of two devastating epidemics of cholera in 1831 and 1848, a few English physicians noted that the dreaded diseases often cropped up in rivertowns downstream from the initial outbreak. To a few daring minds, it suggested the outrageously unorthodox notion that water might be the carrier of cholera. One of these was Dr. John Snow, a London physician. A sudden outbreak of cholera in 1853 gave him an opportunity to test the theory by mapping the occurrences of the cholera cases. Snow found they seemed to have one thing in common. All were in households which drew their water from one well located on Broad Street in the Soho district. As he did not know how to eliminate an infectious agent in water, he proposed that the pump handle of the Soho well be removed. City officials decided to test his hypothesis. The epidemic, consequently was quickly brought under control and probably saved hundreds if not thousands of human lives. Although it was three decades before the etiology of cholera was established by the German bacteriologist, Robert Koch, sanitary engineers in England soon focused their efforts on providing hygienic sources of municipal water. By 1883, when the causal agent of the disease was isolated and studied, cholera had been effectively curbed in both England and the United States.

As bacteriological diseases like cholera, dysentery, diphtheria, and typhoid no longer plague American cities, we take it for granted that drinking water will not make us ill although more than 2,000 communities are discharging raw human sewage into our waterways. The practice may be deplored, but there is little concern about water-borne disease. The average city dweller assures himself that he and his family are safe because their water is chlorinated. Shortly after the Second World War, however, sanitary officials were shaken out of such complacency and began to suspect that conventional water treatment techniques were not effective against certain pathogenic (disease bearing) agents. Chlorine is capable of eliminating harmful bacteria, but are the viruses—pathogens of hepatitis, polio, and cancer—passing through the chemical screen?

With the advent of World War II and large concentrations of soldiers, army doctors were naturally concerned about the traditional camp epidemics of infectious hepatitis, generally known as jaundice, since the eyeballs and skin of its victims acquire a yellowish cast. Fortunately infectious hepatitis is seldom fatal, but it is almost always extremely debilitating. Despite an intensive research program, 180,000 American soldiers were hospitalized by this infection during the last World War.

Experiments of the medical experts revealed that hepatitis viruses survived chemical treatment unless the chlorine level was significantly increased. The laboratory work was supported by studies of hepatitis epidemics. The reports included analyses of outbreaks in Grangesburg, Sweden, where 400 persons succumbed to the disease and in the spectacular New Delhi, India, epidemic which affected 30,000 residents in a city of two million. In both cases the highly suspected sources of infection were the municipal supplies of water.

A documented case of hepatitis from drinking water occurred in a small town in Daviess County, Kentucky, where an outbreak occurred in several adjacent houses. Investigation revealed that the disease was almost certainly caused by the movement of the pathogens from a single septic tank to a series of seven neighboring wells. Fluorescene dye was introduced into the toilet of the suspected house. Within a short time the dye appeared in the nearby wells.

Is there cause for national alarm? Not yet, perhaps, but there are indications that infectious hepatitis is becoming more prevalent. In 1954 some 50,000 cases were reported. The disease apparently declined in the following years and hit a low of 15,000 known cases in 1957. The ebb, however, was followed by an alarming rise, and in 1962 there were 73,000 victims.

Far more important, water contamination may be a cause or contributing factor in the generation of cancer. We are pouring nine identified carcinogens into the air every time we start our autos. Meanwhile, we are also injecting hundreds of chemicals into our waterways including DDT, nitrochlorobenzene, pyridine, detergents, diphenyl ether, nitriles, and substituted benzenes, according to studies made at the Public Health Service's Sanitary Engineering Center in Cincinnati. "Not only do waste treatment processes fail to remove many of these contaminants," says A. J. Anderson of the Public Health Service, "but water purification processes are ineffective."

Among the carcinogens that have been identified in our sources of water are such pesticides as DDT, dieldrin, and chlordane in addition to the aromatic hydrocarbons, benzopyrene and benzanthracene. At least three carcinogenic elements—arsenic, beryllium, and chromium—are found in water. Water contamination by radioactive elements—iodine, strontium, cesium—is well documented and widely known. One of the sinister aspects of nuclear fallout and pesticides is their accumulation in living tissue and the transfer of these concentrations from creature to creature in the food chain that binds humans to the remotest plankton of the sea. The effects of these accumulations throughout a lifetime are not yet known and considerable research remains to be done.

The results of a study of water sources in Holland suggest one possibility. The Dutch scientists found that cancer mortality was lower in communities with a municipal water system than in communities without one, and that towns getting water from wells had a lower cancer death rate than municipalities drawing water from rivers. The statistical evidence strongly suggests that polluted water increases the probability of humans contracting cancer. Dr. Wilhelm C. Hueper, one of the foremost authorities on environmental cancer, is less cautious in warning "with the rapidly increasing urbanization and in- dustrialization of the country and the greatly increased demand placed on the present resources of water from lakes, rivers, and underground reservoirs, the dangers of cancer hazards from the consumption of contaminated drinking water will grow consid- erably within the foreseeable future."

When one considers that the American Cancer Society has estimated that 45,000,000 Americans now living—approxi- mately one in four—will eventually develop cancer, it is quite evident that we must take a hard look at our environment. When we face the fact that today more school children die of cancer, a rarity early in the century, than of any other disease, it is time to do something.

Three decades before Pasteur and Koch established that water-borne bacteria were the agents of deadly human diseases, London officials prompted by Dr. Snow ended a devastating epidemic of cholera by removing the pump handle of a public well in London's Soho district. If we don't follow their example, cancer may take more lives in this century than cholera has throughout history. If American communities throughout the nation do not immediately begin dismantling the handles of pol- lution pumps, our children's legacy will be foul air, fetid water, yellow eyes, black lungs, and the lesions of malignant tissue.

The facts are in. Now is the time for action.

Chapter 9

air decontamination

IF YOU ever take the opportunity to attend a government hearing on either air or water pollution problems, you will undoubtedly witness a variety of tactics aimed at delaying any action to halt or prevent pollution. The favorite argument for delay is that there is no proof that contamination is hazardous to public health. When contradictory evidence is mounted against this position, another line of resistance is presented— really effective decontamination techniques do not exist, so we must wait patiently for more efficient and cheaper devices to be developed.

Although some pollution problems are difficult and expensive to solve, a large portion of today's contamination can be readily eliminated if we demand that action be taken. In the November 1965 issue of *Fortune*, Edmund K. Faltermayer succinctly sums up our situation: "The U. S. has both the technology and wealth to reduce pollution drastically. Even though thousands of factories are still discharging their wastes into the public air, most of the devices for controlling emissions from industrial plants were invented years ago."

Sulfur dioxide, a pollutant which is extremely annoying as well as dangerous to health, is often used as an example of the futility of pollution control. The gas is formed during the combustion of certain fuels, with coal being the major offender. A large part of the coal mined in this country has a sulfur content of anywhere from one to seven percent, with about two percent considered as the level above which the sulfur gases formed during combustion are a problem. While we cannot yet completely prevent sulfur dioxide from getting out into the atmosphere during combustion, we can do a great deal to minimize the amount that is discharged. This can be done by a judicious combination of the choice of suitable fuel, correct fuel preparation, proper firing, and intelligent site location.

In many cases, coal can be replaced by oil or gas with little or no sulfur content. If coal must be used, an effort can be made to obtain a coal with a low sulfur content. Then, at least in the case of the large coal users, the sulfur content can be reduced by appropriate physical treatment. About one-quarter to one-half of the sulfur is present in the form of discrete particles of inorganic materials such as pyrites, which are iron disulfide. This portion of the sulfur can be removed by grinding the coal to a very small particle size before it is used. At that point, the inorganic sulfur can be removed physically. The balance of the sulfur is present in the form of complex organic compounds, and present-day technology has not yet determined how to remove it economically before burning. A substantial fraction of the sulfur dioxide produced during burning can then be removed by techniques such as electrostatic precipitators, washers or acid production. The offensive aspects of the remaining sulfur dioxide can be minimized by selecting a plant site far removed from areas that are harmed by sulfur compounds. Finally, high smoke stacks can be constructed to disperse offensive concentrations long before they reach locations where they might cause problems. In recognition of this problem, a large sum is being spent by the Federal government and industry for research on better ways to remove sulfur from coal.

In the primary metal and metal product industries, furnaces can be equipped with wet washers, electrostatic precipitators, or high temperature filters to reduce dusts and fumes. Wet or dry mechanical separators can also be used at sintering plants to minimize dust emissions. Coal washing, improved equipment design, and better firing practices can improve operation efficiencies and eliminate pollution from coke ovens. Dusts and fumes from foundry and milling operations can be controlled by bag filters.

Hydrocarbon emissions from storage tanks at petroleum refineries can be reduced by a change in tank construction. Proper maintenance can reduce losses through equipment leakage, and waste water separators can be covered to eliminate evaporation losses. Gaseous discharges from boilers and process heaters can be reduced by limited use of the waste products of fuel. Solid emissions from catalyst regeneration stacks can be minimized by using mechanical collectors or electrostatic precipitators.

Leakage of toxic gases and vapors in the chemical industries can be reduced by proper equipment maintenance. Scrubbers can be installed on vents from all reactors, holding tanks, and cooling towers. Dusts from driers and milling operations can be controlled by a variety of methods including most types of particulate control devices.

The major problem in stone, clay, and glass product industries is dust from rotary kilns. The dust can be reduced by using inertial precleaning devices, followed by high temperature cloth collectors or electrostatic precipitators. Odors generated in processing food can be combatted by combustion or the use of scrubbers. Mercaptan odors from paper manufacturing can be reduced by combustion and scrubbing with oxidized black liquor. Fly ash from electric power generating plants can be controlled with mechanical collectors and electrostatic precipitators.

While the cost of pollution abatement equipment is relatively low in most cases, there are exceptions in which it can form an appreciable part of the total equipment cost. Then there may be justification for seeking another approach to the problem. On the other hand, air purification equipment sometimes results in sizable savings or even an additional profit, since pollution control frequently leads to improved processes and greater plant efficiency. The sulfur gases emitted from smelters, for example, can be recovered and converted to fertilizer. In September 1965,

Consolidated Edison of New York announced the development of a technique for converting recovered fly ash into cinder block that can be sold at a profit.

A major source of urban filth is the open burning of garbage, refuse leaves, and junk. It is estimated that we dispose of 150 million tons of trash and garbage a year. About half of this amount is burned, much of it out in the open or in crude incinerators. This practice can be fought by legal prohibitions. Since there are sufficient economic alternatives, there is no valid justification for open burning anywhere in the United States. A reasonable alternative for garbage disposal is sanitary land fill. In addition to eliminating a smoke nuisance and a health hazard, this method produces new areas for local land use. Instead of local burning of autos and construction rubble, central incinerators which serve a large number of garbage and salvage operations should be used. Modern incinerators minimize the contamination of community air and provide a highly efficient method of recovering metals for reuse.

Leaf burning, like backyard incineration, has been banned in many cities which have provided a leaf removal service. This is one of the simplest means of reducing municipal pollution. For relatively little money, a city government can purchase trucks and vacuum equipment to haul the leaves away. All that is required is the willingness of home owners to pay a small increase in their property taxes.

Ironically, the emission of dark smoke from residential heating plants often indicates that furnace combustion is inefficient —with a resultant increase in the home owner's fuel bill. To reduce costs, a landlord or building manager can purchase "smokeless" fuel. He can also improve his firing methods or equipment to increase combustion efficiencies. Consumers should purchase coal or oil with the lowest sulfur content possible. When feasible, gas should be used for space heating, as it produces relatively few effluents.

Unfortunately, the problem of controlling automobile exhaust is far more difficult. In terms of tonnage, this is the largest source of air pollution. A number of proposals have been made which involve substituting diesel, turbine, or electric power plants for the gasoline internal combustion engine. This does not seem practicable, at least not for the next few decades. Our best immediate solution is the development of methods and devices for reducing exhaust emissions. There are now three different ways in which this is done.

The first way—admittedly only a partial solution—is the use of vents leading from the crankcase to the engine. This device, which costs about 15 dollars, is technically sound and removes about 30 percent of the total emissions from auto exhaust. It is now required for all new automobiles in New York and California. An attempt to require its installation on all used automobiles in California met with such strong resistance by the owners of the old cars that the ordinance has been shelved. Because the device reduces pollution and is rather inexpensive, it should be standard equipment on all automobiles. It is an easy and ready method for reducing urban smog throughout the nation. The technology exists. All that is required is legislative action and public support.

A second and more important solution to the problem of auto emissions is to cut down the quantity of exhaust gases by the installation of catalytic or afterburner devices. This approach has been the subject of a great deal of research and development by a number of companies. Today there are several available devices that reduce exhaust gases to the limits set by the State of California. This equipment sells for about 75 to 100 dollars per car. While it does the job when new, there is some question about its effectiveness over a long period of time. One year is the best present estimate as to how long afterburners can operate without needing maintenance to restore maximum performance. To further complicate matters, there is a shortage of mechanics who are qualified to repair these gadgets. A recent California survey showed that only one out of every three garage mechanics knew what to do about them. In spite of these problems, one could anticipate that after a reasonably short initial period, the devices would be operational and that maintenance problems would have been solved.

A much simpler and less costly solution has been found, however, which may make these devices obsolete even before they are used. Each of the major automobile manufacturers has modified its engine so that the emission of exhaust gas now conforms to the California regulations. The additional price per new car is cheaper than the addition of the catalytic or afterburner devices, and the maintenance required appears to be slight. Starting with 1966, all new cars sold in California will meet the State's requirements for exhaust gases, primarily by engine modification. The additional cost to the car buyer is moderate, and a major step towards minimizing the smog problem has been taken.

The General Services Administration has decreed that all new cars bought by the United States Government will have to meet the California exhaust regulations. Other state and municipal bodies are considering taking the same step, and it is hoped there will be enough demand for the automobile manufacturers to find it less troublesome and more economical to treat all their new cars in this manner.

There is room for a great deal of argument about the abatement effectiveness of these techniques. All of the undesirable contaminants are not affected equally; some are barely affected; others are reduced substantially. Once again, the argument is between those who do not want to do anything at all until the problem can be solved 100 percent and those who believe that a step toward any reduction of pollutants is desirable and will immediately benefit our health and comfort. The latter group appears to be gaining the majority, and the result is that the tide of the war against auto pollution should start to turn in the reasonably near future. It will not be a dramatic turn. The effect will be relatively small at first and then will begin to increase as the number of modified 1966 automobiles and subsequent models form an increasing portion of the total number of cars on the highways in California. The first year or two may be discouraging because the results won't be immediately apparent. During this time one may expect an all-out effort by opponents of automobile exhaust pollution control to abandon the whole thing.

There is another encouraging factor to be considered. Research is continuing to improve these techniques for reducing pollution emission, and as better techniques are developed the amount of exhaust pollutants allowed by law will diminish. Eventually, almost all harmful automobile exhaust will be under control.

One further consideration must be mentioned. This is the question of whether or not these exhaust pollution control requirements should be required on a state by state basis, or whether they should be handled in a uniform national manner. Late in 1965, Congress decided to make these requirements nationwide by enacting legislation that will allow the Secretary of Health, Education and Welfare to set up exhaust pollution control requirements starting in 1968, and to establish a new government laboratory to designate reasonable standards as well as develop methods of attaining them. For several reasons, this approach is the only realistic one. First of all, it is unfair to automobile manufacturers to expect them to cope with 50 different sets of requirements. The cost and time of equipping each automobile differently, depending on its destination, are prohibitive. From the manufacturers' point of view, one national requirement by which they must abide would be the only reasonable approach. From the point of view of the individual states, the problems associated with licensing, inspection, and enforcement are overwhelming. The question of interstate movement of automobiles and the pollution of the air of a state that requires devices by automobiles and trucks from a state that does not require them would be a major problem throughout the nation. Most states have deliberately avoided this problem in the hope that the national government would solve it for them. Air pollution recognizes neither geographical nor political boundaries. In the case of the automobile, it is especially obvious that it must be tackled on a national scale by the Federal government.

Chapter 10

water treatment

SOME OF the techniques for eliminating harmful water pollutants generated by human and industrial activity have been known for years. They can be applied easily, especially in cleaning up household wastes. In the case of contamination from industrial sources, the problem frequently is more difficult because manufacturing processes change, and the contaminants generated by them are complex compounds that are not well understood. Nevertheless, if sufficient care is taken, most effluents can be removed prior to discharge into a waterway or prevented from contaminating waste water in the first place. This means good water management consists essentially of effective municipal and industrial housekeeping.

The bulk of pollutants generated by humans can be eliminated from our streams simply by prohibiting the direct discharge of sewage into our waterways, by ending the use of most septic systems in cities and suburban areas, by building sewage treatment plants that utilize adequate procedures, and by separating sanitary and storm sewers. None of these answers is new. All have been known for a long time, but they are applied to a shockingly inadequate degree. This is clearly illustrated by U.S. Public Health Service figures on municipal sewage treatment, published in the May 30, 1964, issue of *Chemical Week* (see table following), as well as by Robert Rickles' excellent monograph on pollution control.*

MUNICIPAL SEWAGE TREATMENT AND POPULATION AFFECTED

Type of Treatment	Percent of Population
None	8.2
Cesspool, septic tanks, etc.	34.2
Sewage Plants with less than primary treatment	1.3
Sewage Plants primary treatment only	18.2
Sewage Plants with intermediate treatment	4.1
Sewage Plants with secondary treatment	34.0
Sewage Plants with tertiary treatment	too few to count

These figures indicate that about 10 percent of our sewage gets no treatment at all, 34 percent receives only natural biological breakdown and dilution, 23 percent is given substandard municipal treatment, and only 34 percent is adequately decontaminated by secondary treatment.

The oldest and least efficient system in use today for the disposal of human wastes is the septic tank. Normally built of brick, concrete, or steel, it is buried in the ground some distance from the dwelling it services at a depth sufficient to maintain the temperature of its contents above 60 degrees. The sewage that is brought into the tank by pipes from the house decomposes through bacterial action at that temperature or above. Periodically part of the accumulated wastes are discharged into distributing pipes and allowed to seep into the soil where further bacterial action presumably completes the elimination of contaminants.

Septic tanks rarely function satisfactorily. Most of these systems rapidly become inefficient after a short time. The tank and pipes get clogged, corrode, or break. More important, the permeability of the ground is often very poor and the soil soon becomes saturated with sewage. When this occurs, the land and nearby ground water, including sources for drinking, become

* Robert Rickles, "Pollution Control," Chemical Process Monograph No. 10, Noyes Development Corporation, 1965.

polluted by human wastes. Frequently this condition is easily perceived by smell and sight in most revolting ways. Such failure would not occur if the system were planned properly. First, the septic tank should be installed only in soil with good permeability. The site should be large enough to be able to absorb the sewage without saturating the locality. Sources of water supply, needless to say, must not be situated near the septic tank. Finally, the tank and associated pipelines must be cleaned out periodically.

These requirements usually are not met, often not even on farms where this type of waste disposal usually is an absolute necessity. When installed in a suburban area, as is often done in new housing developments, it is rarely possible to construct a series of septic tanks that will safely handle human wastes. Once upon a time this was not true, but since World War II began our population has increased 50 percent. Most of this increase has taken place in metropolitan regions. Often the greatest growth occurs in unincorporated areas where sanitation control is nonexistent. Consequently, bad community planning automatically generates a dangerous pollution situation.

Today, septic tanks should not be installed when it is possible to have a modern sewage system. They should be permitted only as a last resort and only under the conditions cited above. In suburban areas, particularly in housing developments, this means that septic systems should not be allowed on lots smaller than one acre, and even then only when permeation tests indicate the prospective home site can handle the calculated seepage. If there are more than fifty homes in the development, a municipal sewage system must be a requisite. Strict adherence to these regulations would eliminate over 75 percent of the septic systems now existing in this country. These are stringent restraints, but with an anticipated population of 250 million by 1980, they are essential to the nation's health and welfare.

Municipal sewage treatment plants service the majority of Americans today. Broadly speaking, there are three types of treatment: primary, secondary, and tertiary.

Primary treatment consists of removing all solids except very fine particles from the sewage. This is done by first settling out the sand and then passing the sewage through a screen to remove large suspended particles. The solids that go through the screen are mostly organic in nature and are then removed by allowing them to settle out in large tanks. Often, chemicals are added to speed up the settling out process, and the procedure is called *flocculation*. The settled out material (sludge) is then "digested" to reduce its volume for ease of handling. This digestion operation involves bacterial action on the sludge. The digested sludge is then dewatered by use of either sand beds, presses, vacuum filters, or centrifuges. Next it is dried by applying heat, and finally the sludge is disposed of by any one of a number of methods that include incineration, lagooning, land fill, dumping, or the production of fertilizer.

Secondary treatment is the biological degradation of the organic matter that remains in waste water after primary treatment and the settling of colloidal organic matter. It involves the use of trickling filters made of gravel beds, digesting microorganisms in activated sludge, and aeration techniques.

Tertiary treatment, a recent technological development, removes material not biologically degraded during previous stages. The phosphorous and nitrogen nutrients that promote algae growth and the eutrophy of lakes and rivers can be inhibited by tertiary techniques. The advanced methods of tertiary treatment include absorption, foaming, chemical oxidation, and aeration in oxidation ponds.

In the richest and most powerful nation on earth, secondary sewage treatment ought to be the minimum standard for all municipalities. The required plant equipment is neither experimental nor mysterious, and, compared to our expenditures for nonessentials such as tobacco and liquor, it is extremely inexpensive. Such a system is especially economical when it is sizable, since the cost drops rapidly with increasing capacities. Rickles estimates that waste treatment operating costs can be reduced from 20 cents per-thousand-gallons in a 10,000 gallon-per-day system to 3.7 cents in a treatment plant that handles 10

million gallons daily. Similarly total costs, including amortiza‑
tion of equipment, drop from 60.3 cents to 13.7 cents for each
1,000 gallons of treated sewage.

These economies dictate the establishment of fairly substan‑
tial operations. This is quite feasible for our large cities.
Smaller cities can achieve similar economies by sharing central‑
ized facilities that serve a number of municipalities. In rural
areas, cooperation on a multicounty scale may be required. Un‑
fortunately, this is frequently unattainable due to distrust of
such cooperative municipal or county enterprises which invoke
the spectre of "big government." Many communities, conse‑
quently, pour raw sewage into our waterways rather than risk
the loss of "independence." It is a price that we no longer can
afford to pay for local autonomy, and this antiquated attitude
must be replaced by a realistic concern for our water resources
and the beauty of our lakes and streams.

A more expensive antipollution measure that must even‑
tually be applied to all our communities is the construction of
separate storm and sanitary sewers. When they are combined,
all of the material in the sewer goes through the treatment
plant. During and after heavy rain, the total accumulation is
too much for the plant to handle, and a good deal of the com‑
bined rainwater and sewage bypasses the plant and goes di‑
rectly into the stream that normally receives treated effluents.
The result is a massive injection of sewage into the waterway.
It would be much better to treat only the sanitary wastes and
send the rainwater directly into the stream. Today, storm
runoff debris is very minor compared to municipal and indus‑
trial waste disposal and for the time being can be discharged
directly into a waterway. When the more serious pollution prob‑
lems of a community have been solved, then the citizenry may
wish to consider methods for primary treatment of storm
runoff to remove leaves, refuse, and other solid debris.

While the detergent problem has been one of the most dra‑
matic pollution problems, we are now at the threshold of greatly
reducing its nuisance. The large masses of foam and scum that
have made our waterways unsightly are caused by synthetic de‑

tergents which are not *biodegradable*. In other words, they are highly resistant to the natural biological degradation that occurs in water and therefore remain essentially unchanged. When churned or agitated in our streams and at our water taps, they readily foam up. Soapy tap water has been especially prevalent in many areas that depend on septic tanks for waste disposal.

West Germany solved this problem by banning such synthetic detergents from the market. This is rapidly cleaning up German rivers. Unfortunately, it is also resulting in economic hardship to the detergent manufacturers and a reduction in the housewife's cleaning power. In this country, the government chose to give detergent manufacturers an opportunity to voluntarily develop detergents that can be degraded by bacteria and put them into general use within a reasonable time limit. Already the new biodegradable detergents are appearing on the market. By the end of 1966 their production should be plentiful enough for the Federal government to ban the use of nonbiodegradable cleaners without significantly disturbing an important sector of the American economy. As a result, it is likely that within the next three to five years, the foam nuisance will be completely eliminated. This demonstrates the effectiveness of genuine cooperation between industry and government.

Good industrial housekeeping is as important as the efficient operation of municipal sewage treatment. One unusual but sometimes highly effective procedure is to seek new processing methods. For example, the development of the soda, magnesia, and ammonia sulfite pulping processes evolved primarily because of the unsolvable stream-pollution by the older lime process. While major changes are seldom feasible, minor changes in processing often can alleviate pollution problems.

Another inplant technique for waste reduction consists of salvaging materials normally lost in waste water or recovery of byproducts in the industrial operations. Often this can be rewarding because of savings in cost of waste treatment or in the production of a profitable product from the salvaged raw material.

The most promising and broadly applicable solution, however, involves the reuse of water. As James M. Quigley, Assistant Secretary of Health, Education and Welfare, made clear at a session of the National Technical Task Committee on Industrial Wastes at San Francisco in 1964, "We have got to take the water we have and use it, clean it up, use it again, clean it up, use it again. This is not going to be inexpensive, but in many sections of the country, it is going to be inevitable." Where the same water is repeatedly used and treated there are several apparent advantages. For one, the amount of water available to other users increases while the total volume of consumed water decreases. In addition, there is a sharp reduction in the amount of residual matter eventually discharged into a stream. Finally, once the capital equipment costs are amortized, this technique can be much more economical than conventional waste treatment. The application of this system by steel plants in this country and Germany has resulted in a substantial reduction of pollution in the streams used for waste disposal. It promises to be one of the most effective and rational solutions to our current water contamination problems. It can and should be applied much more broadly.

One of the most innocent but destructive water pollutants is neither a chemical poison nor a radioactive material. It is simply heat, also known as *thermal pollution* in technical circles. Heat is highly destructive to marine life, especially to sensitive creatures like trout. Ironically, it is the simplest pollutant to eliminate. It is done by cooling the heated water. As oxygen is liberated during heating, the water should also be aerated. This simply means that the water is cooled by the use of heat exchangers and oxygen is put back into it through use of aerators. Thermal pollution could and should be ended immediately.

In some cases, good housekeeping can keep most, if not all, contaminants out of waste water. Normally, however, industrial plants must treat waste in order to return reasonably clean water to a stream or lake after it has been used in manufacturing. This can be done in three ways: physical, chemical, or biological treatments. Although the pollution problems of industry are considerably different from municipal sewage problems, these three types of water conditioning techniques are similar to primary, secondary, and tertiary treatment in municipal plants.

The physical removal of contaminants (as with municipal treatment) is the least expensive water treatment process. Sedimentation or settling is the most common form of physical treatment, and normally the first step in reconditioning water. In addition, settling is often used in the final stage of treatment prior to discharging effluents into a waterway.

Centrifuging is more expensive than sedimentation, but it is particularly useful in the chemistry industry. It is far quicker than passive settling, but then it requires a greater investment in equipment. A few chemical companies have successfully combined both processes. *Flotation* is a combined physical and chemical technique in which air bubbles and chemicals are injected into water to cause suspended solids to accumulate in a froth at the top of the tank where it is skimmed off.

Wastes from man's operations will rarely be eliminated by physical means alone and, frequently, chemical treatment is required. For example, it is essential that highly acidic or alkaline wastes be neutralized. If oxidation of waste chemicals is required, it can be accomplished by physical aeration, or through powerful oxidizing agents such as ozone, permanganates, dichromates, and peroxides.

The two most common types of biological waste treatment are *aerobic* and *anaerobic*. The first depends on bacteria that require dissolved oxygen. Aerobic processing requires a continuous supply of oxygen to replace what is consumed by microbial metabolism. The methods for getting air into waste water are like those used for aeration in municipal plants. Anaerobic processes take place in the absence of oxygen and the by-products, such as methane, hydrogen sulfide, and ammonia, are extremely noxious. As in municipal treatment plants, primary (physical) and secondary (chemical and biological) treatments produce sludges that must be disposed of. Anaerobic processes are used to reduce the bulk of such sludges and make them less obnoxious.

Refineries are among the largest water users. By allowing oil to be discharged in the water returned to the rivers, they are often the worst polluters. This is another case where the means for correcting pollution are at hand and should be used. Many of the refineries do make it a point to keep the oil content in their waste waters at reasonably low levels by such techniques as biological treatments, improved oil-water separators, decreased use of emulsifying chemicals, and good housekeeping. The biological process is especially interesting since, as pointed out earlier, bacteria and algae have the ability to break various chemical compounds down to harmless ones and to improve the taste and odor of effluents. At least 60 U. S. refineries now use settling to improve waste quality. Twenty others employ trickling filters or the activated sludge process. The state of the art is such that pollution from *all* refineries could almost be eliminated today.

Another good technique for minimizing pollution consists of pooled waste treatment plants. In such an arrangement, several small industries discharge their polluted water to a central treatment plant where the pooled waste water is treated more effectively and economically than if treated by individual plants. The principle here is the same as that employed when a number of municipalities band together in a regional sanitary water district.

In summary then, satisfactory methods of waste treatment are available for most of the industrial processes that contribute to water pollution. Many of these are now in use. Unfortunately, however, effective industrial treatment facilities are not as common as they should be. Many industries are cooperating in pollution prevention, but too many are not. The only fair and effective solution is to establish and enforce national or state laws that require all industries to treat their wastes to specified levels before discharging them into our waterways.

Chapter 11

government action

IT IS EVIDENT that the magnitude of environmental contamination is not a consequence of our inability to abate and prevent air and water pollution. It is a consequence of public ignorance and indifference that is reflected by dilatory, ineffective, or nonexistent legislation and legal action against even the grossest corruption. This is particularly true of air pollution control. The first state regulatory legislation was not passed until 1952. By the middle of 1965, only 17 states had enacted comprehensive enforcement legislation. They are: Alaska, California, Colorado, Delaware, Florida, Hawaii, Idaho, Illinois, Indiana, Louisiana, Maryland, Massachusetts, New Jersey, New York, Oregon, Pennsylvania, and West Virginia.

Fortunately, at that time, 13 other states had similar legislation under development and are expected to institute control actions in the near future if the approval of their state legislatures can be obtained. These are: Alabama, Arizona, Connecticut, Georgia, Kentucky, Missouri, Montana, New Mexico, North Dakota, Ohio, Oklahoma, Tennessee, and Texas. For the most part, however, air pollution legislation passed and under consideration is concerned primarily with technical assistance, advice, and some action against especially severe offenders.

Really effective air pollution control is preventive in nature and is carried out by setting up emission standards for the major pollutants and requiring their observance. The only states which have done this are California and Oregon. Illinois and New York are also in the process of adopting such comprehensive standards. Four other states have standards for one or more pollutants while six additional states have authorized the establishment of emission standards. Only California has motor vehicle emission standards.

State-wide agencies generally function by investigating complaints about air pollution and resolving them, or by encouraging compliance with existing ordinances. Local agencies, in contrast, generally place great emphasis on control and abatement activities. They will frequently require, for example, permits for the installation of new systems which may discharge pollutants. In communities of 200,000 or over, three-quarters of the agencies require plan review, but many of these do so only for combustion equipment and not for other process equipment that may cause pollution. In the smaller communities, only about one-third require a review of plans for equipment that has a potential air pollution hazard.

A recent Senate report on air pollution points out an interesting and unpleasant fact. It seems that since many local programs were originally directed only at smoke control, the personnel employed often were selected for their knowledge of fuel-firing practices. The more diverse and complex sources of pollution, which now represent the major problems of contamination, are often beyond their competence. This is a very gentle way of saying that in many cases the staff responsible for air pollution control is not properly trained. The Federal government has therefore undertaken a program of technically assisting both states and cities through its experts at the Robert Taft Sanitary Engineering Center in Ohio.

The financial picture is even more dismal. In 1961, the most recent year for which reasonably complete figures are available, only 17 states were spending as much as 5,000 dollars per year on air pollution programs. Of a total expenditure of two million dollars, 56 percent was by the State of California, as shown in Table 1.

TABLE 1.   STATE EXPENDITURES

State	Type of Program*	Budget, Fiscal Year 1961
California	Technical assistance and research	$ 661,000
	Motor vehicle pollution control	500,000
Colorado	Technical assistance	10,000
Connecticut	Technical assistance	7,200
Delaware	Comprehensive	18,000
Florida	Technical assistance throughout state	12,000
Special District	Comprehensive in Polk-Hillsborough Countries	50,000
Hawaii	Comprehensive	10,000
Maryland	Conduct studies	37,700
Massachusetts	Comprehensive	20,000
Metropolitan Boston	Regulatory program operated by the State	52,000
Michigan	Technical assistance and studies	20,000
Minnesota	Technical assistance	5,000
New Jersey	Comprehensive	104,000
New York	Comprehensive	228,220
Ohio	Technical assistance and studies	95,000
Oregon	Comprehensive	63,000
Pennsylvania	Comprehensive	60,000
Texas	Technical assistance and studies	22,800
Washington	Technical assistance and studies	24,000
	Total	$1,999,920

*Comprehensive includes regulation (control), technical assistance, studies, etc.

Significantly, in the 17 states with air pollution control programs in 1961, the average annual expenditure was only two cents per capita—less than the average school child spends on candy or gum in a single week although air pollution damage and filth cost most of us about 100 dollars a year. The total of full time personnel employed for this work was 148, with 29 others working on a part-time basis. That isn't enough personnel to run a large hotel or department store.

Although more recent figures on state expenditures aren't available, it's safe to estimate that the total 1965 figure is not more than three or four million dollars, a drop in the bucket compared to the money that must be spent to control the air pollution menace.

The picture was a little brighter on a local level in 1961, when there were 85 agencies budgeting at least 5,000 dollars per year for air pollution control. Of the total expenditure of 8 million dollars, 55 percent was in California in seven local units, with the Los Angeles County Air Pollution Control District accounting for 41 percent of the money spent by local agencies throughout the United States.

Nine states have laws that allow municipal air pollution control agencies to serve an area greater than the municipality itself. For example, the San Francisco Bay Area Air Pollution Control District serves 89 urban places of various sizes. Out of 218 urban locations with greater than 50,000 population as well as a major or moderate air pollution problem, only 119 (55 percent) are served by a control agency.

The following table of local control budgets as of February 1, 1961, also developed by the Senate Committee Staff, shows that even where there are control agencies, the average per capita costs came to a piddling 11 cents a year.

TABLE 2.   LOCAL EXPENDITURES

Local Agency	Population 1960 (thousands)	Staff [1]	Budget (thousands)	Per capita budget (cents)	Staff per 100,000 population
Agencies with budgets of $25,000 or more per year					
1. San Francisco Bay area, Calif.	3,364	31.0	$560	16.7	0.9
2. Los Angeles County, Calif.	5,970	373.0	3,402	57.0	6.3
3. Orange County, Calif.	698	11.0	117	16.8	1.6
4. Sacramento County, Calif.[2]	500	4.0	50	10.0	.8
5. San Bernardino County,	498	8.0	[2]259	52.0	1.6
6. Riverside County, Calif.	302	4.0	67	22.2	1.3
7. San Diego County, Calif.	1,000	4.5	79	7.9	.5
8. District of Columbia[3]	746	6.0	42	5.6	.8
9. Polk-Hillsborough Counties, Fla.[4]	592	4.0	50	8.5	.7
10. Chicago, Ill.	3,512	42.0	364	10.4	1.5
11. Indianapolis, Ind.	469	6.0	38	8.1	1.3
12. Jefferson County (Louisville), Ky.	606	11.0	63	10.4	1.8
13. Baltimore, Md.[3]	922	10.0	70	7.6	1.1

TABLE 2.   LOCAL EXPENDITURES (cont'd.)

Local Agency	Popula-tion 1960 (thousands)	Staff [1]	Budget (thou-sands)	Per capita budget (cents)	Staff per 100,000 population
14. Boston metropolitan district, Mass.	1,998	8.0	52	2.6	.4
15. Detroit, Mich.	1,654	20.0	180	10.9	1.2
16. St. Louis, Mo.	747	13.0	118	15.8	1.7
17. Newark, N.J.[3]	403	10.0	63	15.6	2.5
18. Buffalo, N.Y.[3]	530	6.0	59	11.1	1.1
19. New York, N.Y.	7,710	74.0	734	9.5	1.0
20. Niagara Falls, N.Y.	102	3.0	28	27.4	2.9
21. Syracuse, N. Y.	215	5.0	36	16.7	2.3
22. Cincinnati, Ohio (area)[3]	542	18.0	165	30.4	3.3
23. Cleveland, Ohio	870	23.0	236	27.1	2.6
24. Cleveland Heights, Ohio	62	4.0	28	45.3	6.5
25. Columbus, Ohio	469	7.0	50	10.7	1.5
26. Dayton, Ohio[3]	258	7.0	55	21.3	2.7
27. Allegheny County, Pa.	1,629	18.0	217	13.3	1.1
28. Philadelphia, Pa.	1,971	23.0	166	8.4	1.2
29. Providence, R. I.[3]	206	8.0	31	15.0	3.9
30. Knoxville, Tenn.[3]	110	2.0	25	22.7	1.8
31. Harris County, Tex.[3]	1,243	6.0	42	3.4	.5
32. Salt Lake City, Utah	189	4.0	30	15.8	2.0
33. Richmond, Va.	218	4.0	25	11.4	1.8
34. Milwaukee County, Wis.	733	15.0	128	17.5	2.1
Total or median for group	40,929	802.5	7,629	14.1	1.6
Agencies with budgets of less than $25,000 per year					
1. Birmingham, Ala.	341	2.0	12	3.5	.6
2. Denver, Colo.	494	2.0	15	3.1	.4
3. Dade County, Fla.	935	[5]1.0	5	.5	——
4. Atlanta, Ga.	485	1.0	13	2.7	.2
5. Cicero, Ill.	69	[5]1.0	5	7.2	——
6. Peoria, Ill.	103	1.0	8	7.8	1.0
7. East Chicago, Ind.	58	1.0	11	19.3	1.7
8. Evansville, Ind.	140	1.0	10	7.2	.7
9. Des Moines, Ia.	208	[5]2.0	11	5.3	——
10. McCracken County (Paducah), Ky.	57	1.0	12	20.9	1.8
11. Dearborn, Mich.	112	[5]2.0	5	4.5	——
12. Grand Rapids, Mich.	175	[5]2.0	6	3.4	——
13. Monroe, Mich.	23	1.0	6	26.1	4.3
14. Wayne County, Mich.	2,666	1.5	20	.8	.06
15. Minneapolis, Minn.	478	1.0	11	2.3	.2

TABLE 2.   LOCAL EXPENDITURES (cont'd.)

Local Agency	Population 1960 (thousands)	Staff [1]	Budget (thousands)	Per capita budget (cents)	Staff per 100,000 population
16. Omaha, Nebr.	300	2.0	20	6.7	.7
17. Camden, N. J.	125	1.0	7	5.6	.8
18. Hillside Township, N.J.	21	[5]3.0	5	23.8	——
19. Perth Amboy, N.J.	38	1.0	13	34.2	2.6
20. Trenton, N. J.	114	1.0	5	4.4	.9
21. Illion, N.Y.	10	1.0	5	49.0	1.0
22. Rochester, N.Y.	316	1.0	10	3.2	.03
23. Tonawanda, N.Y.	84	2.0	15	17.9	2.4
24. Watertown, N.Y.	33	1.0	7	21.2	3.0
25. Asheville, N.C.	59	3.0	16	27.2	5.1
26. Charlotte, N.C.	201	2.0	19	9.5	1.0
27. Winston-Salem, N.C.	111	2.0	12	10.8	1.8
28. Akron, Ohio	288	2.0	16	5.6	.7
29. East Cleveland, Ohio	38	1.0	7	18.4	2.6
30. Sandusky, Ohio	32	1.0	7	21.9	3.1
31. Toledo, Ohio	316	2.0	12	3.8	.6
32. Youngstown, Ohio	166	2.0	17	10.3	1.2
33. Zanesville, Ohio	39	1.0	5	12.8	2.6
34. Eugene, Ore.	50	1.0	10	20.0	2.0
35. Portland, Ore.	371	1.0	17	4.6	.3
36. Erie, Pa.	138	2.0	15	10.8	1.5
37. Lehigh Valley, Pa. (area)	278	1.0	14	5.0	.4
38. East Providence, R. I.	42	1.0	8	19.1	2.4
39. Pawtucket, R. I.	81	1.0	5	6.3	1.2
40. Columbia, S.C.	96	1.0	6	6.3	1.0
41. Chattanooga, Tenn.[3]	128	2.0	16	12.5	1.6
42. Kingsport, Tenn.	26	1.0	7	26.6	3.9
43. Memphis, Tenn.[3]	492	2.0	13	2.6	.4
44. Nashville, Tenn.	167	2.0	13	7.9	1.2
45. Roanoke, Va.	97	1.0	11	11.4	1.0
46. Seattle, Wash.	552	1.0	12	2.2	.2
47. Tacoma, Wash.	147	1.0	8	5.4	.7
48. Wheeling, W. Va.	53	2.0	17	32.1	3.8
49. Fond du Lac, Wis.[3]	33	1.0	7	21.4	3.0
50. Green Bay, Wis.[3]	63	1.0	7	11.2	1.6
51. Madison, Wis.	126	2.0	14	11.1	1.6
Total or median for group	10,475	73.5	548	7.8	1.0
Total or median for all agencies	51,404	876.0	8,177	10.8	1.3

[1] Not including clerical personnel.
[2] 1960 fiscal year.
[3] Staff believed to spend considerable time on work other than air pollution.
[4] Operated by the state in which located.
[5] Part time.

In response to state and local inadequacies, Congress passed Public Law 155 in 1955, the first Federal air pollution control program of any consequence. This act provided impetus for government research in air pollution and made provision for grants and contracts to other agencies for additional research. In 1960, a law authorizing a study on motor vehicle exhaust was passed. The net effect of these two laws was to establish a government research program and to provide technical assistance to state and local agencies. This often takes the shape of investigations, recommendations, assistance in starting up local control programs, and training courses.

A major step was taken late in 1963 with the enactment of Public Law 88-206, more popularly known as the Clean Air Act. For the first time, the government assumed authority to take action to solve specific air pollution problems. In addition, Federal funds for government-sponsored research were increased. Finally, the Act made substantial sums of money available to state and local agencies on 2:1 and 3:1 matching bases. This latter portion of the Act has been responsible for an encouraging spurt of activity at state and local levels in an effort to set up air pollution control agencies that are paid for primarily with Federal funds.

As nineteen states report the existence of interstate air pollution problems, they are receiving particular attention. Eleven states have made some sort of arrangement to try to work with neighboring states to solve their problems. The interstate compact recently approved by Illinois and Indiana and now awaiting Congressional approval, provides for punitive legal action, and is the first one with teeth in it. This interstate compact is especially important, because if successful it will serve as the pilot model for other interstate agreements.

As 43 million Americans live in 45 metropolitan areas that cross state boundaries and 20 million others live in 77 metropolitan areas that border on state lines, the principal abatement action authority vested in the Federal government relates to interstate problems. Without an interstate compact, local ordinances and state laws alone are seldom effective in such situations. To correct this, the Clean Air Act provides that the Federal government may take action in the absence of any other effective control. Such action is initiated by calling a conference of parties involved in an air pollution situation, either at the request of one of the governors of the affected state or at the initiative of the Secretary of Health, Education and Welfare. These conferees will usually agree on the cause of the problem and the actions that should be taken to stop it. The information developed at the conference will then be made available to all groups in a position to take action to stop the trouble. After six months, if no satisfactory corrective action has been taken, a public hearing is held. The findings of the Board that conducts the hearing together with their recommendations for corrective action are then sent to the agencies concerned. If action still is not taken within a specified time, the government institutes court action, and appropriate judgments are entered.

The Clean Air Act also encourages cooperative interstate action positively by financing up to three-quarters of the cost of developing, establishing, or improving programs involving two or more states. The available money from the Clean Air Act, however, is far too limited. Illinois, for example, has used up its allotment for funds to the state, Chicago, and Cook County. None of these bodies received as much as they could have used. Even worse, no funds are left for any other Illinois city or county that seeks to expand its air pollution control activity.

Where air pollution is causing problems within one state only, the procedure for Federal participation is the same as interstate problems with two major exceptions. First, the conference can only be called on the request of the governor of the state or at the joint concurrence of the state and municipal air pollution control agencies. Second, the government's action is limited to providing technical assistance or advice on request of the governor as needed by the state in its judicial proceedings. The Federal government can take direct legal action only at the request of the governor. For all practical purposes, therefore, Washington has no control authority over air pollution problems that affect only one state.

While these provisions for direct Federal action are still painstakingly slow and are burdened with many restrictions, they do represent the first actual involvement with enforcement activities. This authority has resulted in moves by many states to try to clean their own houses before the Federal government does it for them. The first interstate conference has already taken place between New York and New Jersey. Other conferences recently called include one requested by Vermont concerning a plant in Ticonderoga, New York, and one by Delaware in connection with a problem originating in Bishop, Maryland.

The most recent Federal legislative action in the field of air pollution control took place on October 1, 1965, when Congress passed a bill amending the Clean Air Act which greatly increased government power in this area. The major new provision is the requirement that the Secretary of HEW shall prescribe practicable standards for the emission of substances from new motor vehicles "as soon as possible". Technological feasibility and economic cost are to be taken into consideration in establishing these standards. A statement by Wilbur J. Cohen, acting secretary of HEW at the time, outlines how this will be implemented:

> Testimony from the automobile industry indicated that control systems could be applied on the 1968 models, and we see no reason to delay the application of standards beyond that period. It is our intention to promulgate our initial regulations in time for application to the 1968 model year. Although the House amendment would permit the application of exhaust standards to diesel-powered vehicles as well, we do not intend to apply standards until we are satisfied that the technology of diesel exhaust control is sufficiently developed.

By 1968, consequently, all new cars will probably be equipped with pollution control devices. How will this affect the smog in our big cities? If one assumes that the net result will be some 50 to 60 percent reduction in the discharge of harmful gases, and that all cars have been properly equipped, auto pollution will be reduced to the current level by 1978. In other words, this action will just about combat the expected *increase* in air pollution due to automobiles—an increase that would have been devastating to many of our larger cities; but the reduction will not improve the present situation.

Recognizing this, Congress also made provision in the bill for the government to accelerate its research effort to find better controls for: 1. hydrocarbon emissions resulting from gasoline evaporation in carburetors and fuel tanks; 2. oxides of nitrogen and aldehydes from gasoline or diesel-powered vehicles; and 3. oxides of sulfur produced by the combustion of *any* type of fuel. This is research that will ultimately lead to a reduction in the *present* amount of pollution. As new information is developed through this research, the emission standards will be tailored accordingly.

The last major new air pollution control action in the 1965 bill gives the secretary of HEW the right to call a conference on *potential* air pollution problems. If the secretary finds that the impending contamination can be legally abated, then he is required to send his findings together with his recommendations for preventing the pollution to the imminent offenders and to the appropriate state, interstate, and local agencies. This is simply an advisory action on the part of the Federal government, but it places responsibility for follow-through on the state and local authorities. Senator Muskie said he did not intend this to "be used as an excuse to avoid enforcement in existing cases and that it not be used to interfere in those states where there are established air pollution control programs." Rather, it allows the government to initiate action in cases that would otherwise go unchallenged because of inactivity or nonexistence of local enforcement agencies.

control of corrupted water

AS WITH air pollution, legal control of water pollution is desirable at a number of different levels in the hierarchy of American government. Some controls may be handled efficiently at a municipal level, others require regional cooperation, some are best carried out at a state or interstate level, while a few can only be effectively controlled on a nationwide basis.

Although water pollution controls are inadequate and need strengthening at every level, there are a number of effective measures being carried out at the local level in many of our municipalities. Probably the most basic and essential control is the prevention of the discharge of untreated human sewage directly into waterways.

Rigid controls over septic systems have been inaugurated by some communities and many relatively large towns and cities today do not allow septic systems within their municipal limits. Others with small populations and large average lot sizes impose stiff requirements for septic tanks. On the other hand, as many as one-half of our communities with less than 5,000 population place few, if any, controls on septic systems. Furthermore, in many large real estate developments set up in unincorporated areas, county regulations formulated for rural conditions are followed, and these are generally inappropriate or feebly enforced.

A very effective and necessary control measure at the municipal level is the establishment of separate storm and sanitary
sewers. Enforcement is exercised by requiring goverment approval of the plans for construction of residential and industrial
buildings. While this requirement is now more prevalent, far
too many communities still build combined systems.

A much more difficult municipal decision is whether or not to
convert an existing combined sewer system into separate
sewers. This is an extremely expensive proposition and is undertaken only when contamination has become intolerable.
Tables 1 and 2 * list cities in this country where the separation
of sewers should be completely or partially undertaken. They
indicate how expensive it is to correct the mistake of having
built combined sewers in the first place. In most cases, the
financing is so great that individual communities need Federal
financial support.

The type of public sewage disposal system used by new homes
is usually controlled by the municipality. In those cases where
the municipality is too small to be effective or where the area of
development is unincorporated, control is exercised by the
county. It determines the type of treatment unit to be used,
specifies the body of water to be used for disposal, and locates
points of discharge. In setting restrictions, officials consider the
eventual type of treatment, the dilution available, and the quality requirements of the final effluent. They also study potential
hazards to maintenance personnel and the public, the reactions
of the discharged material with other materials already present
in the sewers (e.g., cyanides reacting with acids), and damage
to the physical structure of the sewer system itself, such as
corrosion or impediment of flow rates.

On the local level, it is also possible to impose regulations
controlling the discharge of industrial wastes to rivers and
lakes. This is not often done because it introduces an element of
unfair economic competition with industries in communities
without such regulations. Thus this type of control is more often
exercised at the state level.

---

* Rickles, R., "Pollution Control," Noyes Development Corp., 1965.

TABLE 1. ESTIMATED COSTS FOR COMPLETE
SEPARATION OF STORMWATER AND
SANITARY SEWERS

City	Total Project Cost (Millions $)	Cost/Acre ($)	Cost/Capita ($)
Chicago, Ill.	2,300	17,000	482
Cleveland, Ohio	470–700	12,000–18,000	360–535
Concord, N.H.	8	—	280
Detroit, Mich.	1,315		360
Haverhill, Mass.	30	10,500	650
Kansas City, Kans.	20	7,745*	187
Lawrence, Kans.	30	13,500	915
Lowell, Mass	70	12,000	780
Milwaukee, Wis.	425	8,250	440
New Haven, Conn.	10	16,363*	560
New York, N.Y.	4,000	25,000–30,000	492
Portland, Ore.	100–250	3,100– 7,750	260–652
Seattle, Wash.	145	3,890	260
Spokane, Wash.	50	1,800	415
Toronto, Ont.	285	17,000	—
Washington, D.C.	214	18,000	250
Total	9,662**	12,427**	468**

* —Based on actual project cost.
**—Using the average costs for those cities reporting ranges. U.S. only.

Source: 1. Water Pollution Control Federation
2. U.S. Public Health Service

In summary, then, the municipality exercises its most effective control over human sewage and, except in our largest cities, a relatively small degree of control over industrial wastes. A metropolitan area including numerous smaller municipalities can exercise the most effective control on a regional or county basis, since a few communities can affect the entire urban population. This potential problem can be solved by a regional approach that takes the form of a federation or metropolitan district limited specifically to sanitary water control.

The Sanitary District in the Greater Chicago Metropolitan Area is an excellent example of the value of a regional sanitary water control facility. While the City of Chicago can control its own water pollution problems satisfactorily, there are over two hundred other municipalities in surrounding Cook County. Most of them do not have sufficient funds to build their own facilities.

TABLE 2. ESTIMATED COSTS FOR PARTIAL SEPARATION
OF STORMWATER AND SANITARY SEWERS

City	Total Project Cost ($)	Cost/Acre ($)	Cost/Capita ($)
Des Moines, Iowa	25,000,000	7,800	170
Elmhurst, Ill.	8,770,000	—	237
Eugene, Ore.	3,410,000	3,100	76
Findlay, Ohio	15,108,000	—	500
Granite City, Ill.	13,200,000	4,900	330
Hannibal, Mo.	613,000	—	43
Kendallville, Ind.	969,000	—	143
Lafayette, Ind.	5,024,000	—	120
La Porte, Ind	9,187,000	—	437
Lathrup Village, Mich.	961,500	—	302
Louisville, Ky.	30,538,000	—	73
Michigan City, Ind.	3,500,000	—	95
Minneapolis, Minn.	30,000,000	3,040	69
Mishawaka, Ind.	4,392,000	972	129
Napa, Colorado	1,549,000	640	52
Sedalia, Mo.	4,470,000	—	213
Seattle, Washington	69,000,000	1,860	124
Tacoma, Washington	7,960,000	—	53
Total	233,651,500	3,187*	176*

*Average

Source: 1. Water Pollution Control Federation
2. U. S. Public Health Service

Without this area-wide control system, these municipalities
would not only pollute their own waters, but they would impose
an intolerable burden on Chicago. By using this sort of a regional arrangement, not only does the city benefit, but a large number of adjoining suburbs get an inexpensive, highly efficient
treatment of their wastes.

Every one of our states has laws to control water pollution
and all have official agencies to enforce these laws. In some
cases, enforcement authority rests within the State Department
of Public Health. In others it lies with a separate body created
specifically for that purpose. There are usually two distinct
parts to state laws concerning water pollution. One provides
that a permit must be obtained from the control agency for any
new or increased discharge of wastes, while the other gives the

control agency authority to promulgate rules and regulations, to conduct hearings, and to issue cleanup orders.

The state control agency usually sets standards for industrial discharges, makes inspections to determine compliance, and institutes legal action when required. The state plays a very important role in collecting and analyzing data on water supply and pollution within the state limits and in giving technical aid and information to local governments and industries seeking ways to treat their wastes. The state agency also reviews plans for local sewage treatment plants and maintains surveillance over their operations. Some states have established standards for the discharge of wastes into streams and lakes. Most of them, however, either have not done so or have vague and ineffective standards.

The effectiveness of state agencies varies widely and often reflects the amount of money devoted to water pollution control. This ranges from less than one cent per year for each person in a state up to 24 cents per person. Pennsylvania spends more than most states because it has had an acid mine drainage problem in its waterways since 1937. The problem still has not been solved, and the state has recently allocated a substantial sum of money for research into a novel approach to eliminating acid drainage. In New York, citizens dazed by a water shortage and shocked by the magnitude of contamination in the state, overwhelmingly passed a 1.7 billion dollar water pollution abatement bond issue in 1965.

State spending on water pollution control is indicated in Table 3. The list of 1963 expenditures has been prepared by the United States Public Health Service. These expenditures include grants from the Federal government, so that, in many cases, the state's share was less than indicated.

Unfortunately, there are few rivers of any consequence located entirely within one state. Control of pollution, therefore, frequently must be exercised by some form of interstate agency. Some of these interstate agencies have regulatory powers and can set standards of water quality for the rivers and streams in their jurisdiction. They also can legally require the adoption of

TABLE 3.   STATE EXPENDITURES FOR
WATER POLLUTION CONTROL

Over $1,000,000	$500,000-$1,000,000	$300,000-$500,000	$200,000-$300,000	$100,000-$200,000	Under $100,000
California	Florida	Colorado	Georgia	Alabama	Alaska
New York	Ohio	Illinois	Indiana	Arkansas	Arizona
Penna.	Texas	Mass.	Kansas	Conn.	Dist. Col.
		Michigan	Maryland	Delaware	Idaho
		New Jersey	Miss.	Hawaii	Montana
			No. Car.	Iowa	Nebraska
			Tennessee	Kentucky	Nevada
			Virginia	Louisiana	No. Dakota
			Wash.	Maine	So. Dakota
			Wisconsin	Minn.	Utah
				Missouri	Vermont
				New Hamp.	Wyoming
				New Mex.	
				Okla.	
				Oregon	
				Rhode Is.	
				So. Car.	
				West Va.	

whatever treatment methods are necessary to achieve these standards. Perhaps the most effective body of this type is the Ohio River Valley Water Sanitation Commission (ORSANCO), established by a compact between all the states bordering the Ohio River. This agency has a staff that keeps close watch over the discharge of pollutants into the river and calls problems to the attention of a governing commission empowered to take legal action to enforce its control standards.

Today the Ohio River is gradually being cleaned up. Furthermore, despite rapid expansion of industrial operations, the Ohio is now cleaner than it has been in years. The success of ORSANCO has encouraged the development of other interstate groups with regulatory powers. One is the Interstate Sanitation Commission in the New York Metropolitan Area. Another is the Delaware River Basin Commission. These may well be the start of the effective cleanup of this country's largest rivers.

Many other interstate bodies are primarily advisory in nature. Their function is to investigate pollution problems, sample waterways, and set water quality standards which member states are urged to achieve. The Interstate Commission on the Potomac River Basin and the New England Interstate Water Pollution Control Commission are organizations of this type.

Another type of interstate cooperative effort consists of informal or formal regional groups, established on the basis of a watershed or some other specific geographical area. Such groups meet periodically to work on quality standards and water uses. This is being done in the Arkansas River Compact, the Pecos River Compact, the Red River Drainage Basin Interstate Sanitation Committee, the Pacific Northwest Pollution Control Council, the Missouri River Regional Council, and the Upper Mississippi River-Great Lakes Boards of Public Health Engineers.

The Federal position in the field of water corruption is similar to its activities relating to air pollution. Since the water resources problem has been of national concern for a longer period, however, more progress has been made in cleaning up rivers and streams.

Federal water pollution control is vested in the Department of Health, Education and Welfare. The bulk of the activity at present consists of sponsoring research designed to minimize the problem and recommending solutions to state and local agencies. Most of the research is conducted by government scientists and engineers in Washington and at the Robert Taft Sanitary Engineering Center in Cincinnati. In addition, the government is now proceeding with plans to set up seven regional laboratories for water pollution research. Grants are also given to other organizations that wish to do research in this field.

As with air pollution, new legislation designed to increase government control was passed by Congress in 1965. Federal funds for aid to municipalities constructing waste treatment plants were increased by the 1965 Water Quality Act. It raised the total amount to 150 million dollars annually for the next two years. Of the first 100 million each year, the maximum for an individual project is 1,200,000 dollars, while up to 4,800,000 can be allocated to a project that will serve a number of communities. This is a new feature in government legislation. It is designed to encourage small communities to get together for one large sewage treatment plant that would benefit them all. The Clear Lake, Texas, area described earlier is a case where this provision could be very helpful.

There is no restriction on the size of individual grants that may be made from the remaining 50 million dollars each year except that the law specifies this money shall be allotted on the basis of population. It is designed to correct an injustice under the previous government program is which assistance went almost exclusively to small cities. For example, it is quite evident that the old limit of 600,000 dollars for an individual sewage treatment plant would be insignificant to New York City where a single pollution control project alone has cost as much as $87.6 million. Now the government is in a position to make a more significant, although still small, contribution to new sewage treatment plants for large metropolitan areas.

Prior to passage of the 1965 law, the Federal government's power to enforce corrective action in severe water pollution cases was very weak, similar to its position for air pollution control. It was limited to interstate pollution situations, and even then only when it could prove danger to the public health and welfare or at the request of a state governor. This meant that no preventive measures could be taken. Instead, the government became involved only when the situation had deteriorated to the point where a menace already existed. This was the situation at the southern end of Lake Michigan where a five-year United States Public Health Service study found that 31 industries and 21 municipalities were dumping hundreds of tons of waste into sluggish waters, thereby endangering the health and welfare of 8 million persons in the area. To correct this situation, a conference was called in 1965 to initiate an abatement program. A technical committee was formed by representatives of Illinois and Indiana as well as the Metropolitan Sanitary District of Greater Chicago, the Federal government, the American Oil Company, and the United States Steel Corporation. In February of 1966 the committee announced that a December 1968 deadline for cleaning up the southern end of the lake had been set.

In a similar manner, an agreement was reached with Kansas City for that municipality to construct waste treatment facilities within a fixed period of time. This action was the result of joint agreement by the Department of Health, Education and Welfare with the states of Kansas and Missouri.

A conference on the Lake Erie problem was held in the fall of 1965. At the first of a series of meetings, representatives from Michigan, Ohio and Indiana agreed to try to control Lake Erie pollution. At a subsequent meeting held in Buffalo, New York, officials of the five heavily industrialized states bordering on the lake agreed to submit remedial construction schedules within six months for new municipal sewage works, industrial waste treatment plants, and other facilities. Plans and specifications were to be completed by August 1966, financing by February 1967, start on construction by August 1967, and completion of the construction by Jan. 1, 1969. The main problem involved in bringing these plans to fruition will be the question of financing, often the most difficult aspect of corrective action.

Another conference called shortly thereafter dealt with the Hudson River. The conferees agreed to a series of steps involving construction of treatment plants from New York to Albany. If carried out, the Hudson River could be open for swimming in less than a decade. Industry was told to "effect maximum reduction" of such wastes as acids and alkalies, oil and tarry substances, and foam producing discharges. The New York officials also called for the submission of plans to separate all storm and sanitary sewers in the area, and to install immediately separate systems in all new building projects.

Perhaps the most controversial and meaningful provision of the Water Quality Act of 1965 allows the Federal government to set water quality standards where needed for interstate waters throughout this country. This is the first "preventive" power given to the Federal government. Opponents protested that this power rightfully belongs to the states. Proponents, on the other hand, pointed out that the increasing pollution, especially in streams that run through several states, is evidence of the inability of state governments to regulate the problem properly, consequently obligating the Federal government to take action. As Federal provisions could be put into effect much sooner than regional cooperation, they pointed out that this is the most effective mechanism for remedial action.

After extensive debate, a compromise was fashioned giving the states until June 30, 1967, to establish water quality standards on interstate waterways identified by the Federal government. The state standards are to be subject to Federal approval. In the absence of effective state standards at the appointed time, the government can initiate a conference procedure involving the affected Federal, state, interstate, municipal, and industrial officials. The state will then be given six months to adopt appropriate water standards as defined at the conference. Failing this, a hearing board representing both the Federal and state governments will be established. This board has the right to recommend standards which then go into effect. The net result, after giving all relevant parties an opportunity to participate in the deliberations, is that standards will be set on all interstate waterways.

As a result of the air and water pollution legislation passed in 1965, the Federal government finally can initiate action designed to prevent both air and water pollution. The conditions in this country still are dismal, but this recent Congressional action and favorable public response are encouraging. It indicates that both the electorate and its representatives are stirring from a deep slumber of political apathy, and that we are at last beginning to realize that clean air and pure water are possible when local, state, and Federal agencies team up for a concerted effort to dismantle the handles of the nation's major pollution pumps.

Chapter 13

consequences of division

AS YOU become aware of the assault of environmental pollution on our health and economy, you may wonder why existing pollution control technology hasn't been used. Why hasn't appropriate legislation been passed? What will happen if we don't take effective action in the near future?

An indictment for the mess in which we find ourselves can be levelled against both industry and government. Industry can be blamed for fighting controls and for spending much too little to reduce its wastes; government is at fault for not effectively legislating against pollution and often not even enforcing what laws and ordinances do exist. The greatest responsibility for environmental corruption, however, lies with the American public for not having insisted on a meaningful reduction of pollution. We have only ourselves to blame for foul air and filthy water.

Industrialists are beginning to realize that their attitude toward pollution control has been negative and intransigent. At public hearings relating to pending legislation, representatives of industry have been guilty of opposing recommended control measures without suggesting reasonable alternatives. Their arguments can be summed up simply: (1) the danger hasn't been proven conclusively; (2) there is a need for more research to develop effective and economic solutions; (3) pollution problems are best handled locally.

A point of view that is normally disguised was expressed in a surprisingly candid manner by an industrial representative at a 1963 Congressional hearing on pending legislation. In response to a Senator's doubt about the witness' concern for public health, he said "Well, actually we are trying to be very realistic and objective in this thing. We have to satisfy our stockholders and return a capital return on our investments, and so we look at these things from an economic standpoint as well as from health standards."

The automobile industry has been particularly singled out for delaying the installation of pollution control equipment years after it was practical. In discussing the new engine modifications by the major automobile manufacturers to control exhaust pollution, S. Smith Griswold, formerly Chief of the Los Angeles Air Pollution Control District and now chief U.S. air pollution control enforcement official, charged that "Everything the industry has disclosed it is able to do today to control automobile exhausts was possible ten years ago." He pointed out that crankcase emissions have been controlled by a method in use at least half a century and that the emission of hydrocarbons and carbon monoxide is being controlled by relatively simple adjustments of the carburetor and ignition systems. He ascribed the decade-long stall to "arrogance and apathy on the part of this, the nation's largest industry. Control of air pollution does not make cars easier to sell; it does not make them cheaper to produce; and it does not reduce comebacks on warranty. To people interested in profits, expenditures for the development and production of exhaust controls are liabilities."

This indictment of the automobile industry by Griswold cannot be taken lightly—and yet, are not auto users as guilty? Can we really expect Detroit manufacturers voluntarily to raise the price of cars if consumers don't care enough to pay the extra cost? In fact, isn't it realistic not to expect corporations to add to the price of new construction or to the cost of plant operation if it is not required by law or public demand? Furthermore, can we reasonably inflate the operational costs of a manufacturer if a competitor in another city or state doesn't have to meet similar requirements, enabling a polluter to undersell a nonpolluter? Certainly industry must shoulder a large share of the blame for the physical corruption that exists today, but the consumer public is also at fault for not protesting and encouraging public officials to translate its gripes into uniform legal requirements on a regional or national level.

Without broad public support, municipal action is often blunted by the fear of antagonizing industrialists. Many community leaders are afraid that an industry may vacate the area rather than abate pollution, leaving a hygienic but impoverished city. This anxiety is often prevalent where relief from pollution is most needed. The opinion that smoky skies and discolored rivers are unavoidable characteristics of prosperity is still widely held by many civic and municipal leaders. This is simply not true, and, if control measures become widespread throughout the country there will eventually be few pollution sanctuaries for industry. In one case, for example, a company left Cincinnati rather than modify its industrial operations to abate air pollution. The concern moved to Los Angeles. Soon after relocation, the city initiated abatement activities and the company faced even more vigorous antipollution measures than those from which it had fled. This should become a common occurrence.

Often the effectiveness of government action has been diluted by confusion and conflict among Federal officials. In this regard, the President's Science Advisory Committee has stated that:

> Arrangements to deal with pollution have grown on a piecemeal basis, with organizations, programs, and legislation created when problems became evident or critical. With this background it is not surprising that current organization is a hodgepodge with responsibilities widely separated among government agencies, and some unassigned. Some pollutants are dealt with on the basis of the environmental medium in which they occur, for example, pollutants in air and water; others are dealt with on the basis of the kinds of effect they have, for example, toxic materials in food; some are dealt with on the basis of their sources, for example, artificially radioactive materials.

This multiplicity of agencies with overlapping or conflicting authority also exists in state, county, and municipal government. Thus political divisions undoubtedly have contributed to New York's water crisis. Several different groups of water experts long ago advised municipal and state officials to clean up the Hudson and use it as a dependable source of water for New York City. Had that advice been taken at the time, there couldn't be a critical shortage of potable water today.

Even Governor Rockefeller, who is cognizant of the dangers of pollution and has expressed himself forcefully on the subject, is against Federal control in his state under any circumstances. Last year at a hearing on pollution in Lake Erie he rationalized his position by contending that New York's effluents remain in New York, and although he would accept Federal funds to assist a cleanup of the lake he would resist Federal control. Senator Robert Kennedy, who said that Public Health Studies on the subject were "an indictment against New York," was in sharp disagreement with the Governor. Obviously, if even the Governor of New York is not yet convinced of the need to approach the Lake Erie problem on a regional basis, New York and the rest of the nation are seriously divided. Unfortunately, we can't afford a divided house on the issue of environmental contamination. The magnitude of pollution is now so great—and daily getting worse—that it is imperative for industry and government at all levels to cooperate fully in restoring the integrity of our environment. Anything less could be catastrophic—a fact which becomes evident when you consider the projections of population growth and industrial expansion, and the nation's future needs.

Between 1900 and 1962, total water use in the United States increased eightfold to 343 billion gallons daily, while the population only doubled. In 1965, the U.S. required some 371 billion gallons of water each day, while our available supply of water was only 315 billion gallons per day—already 56 billion gallons a day less than current demands. Our needs are expected to double again in the next two decades, and by the year 2000 the country will require 1,000 billion gallons every day. Making allowances for technological advances and improved conservation practices, and taking into account all potentially available water resource development projects, we will only be able to manage 650 billion gallons a day by the end of the century. This will be 350 billion gallons less than the expected daily need. If we allow ourselves to fall into this dilemma, one can well imagine the resultant national panic and the enormity of Federal crash programs. It could make the 60 billion dollar defense budget seem modest.

Let us examine projected changes in the water situation from another point of view. Consider the discharge of wastes from municipalities and industries. Since 1900, the municipal waste load discharged into the nation's waters has been increased by an additional load from 51 million people. This will grow to 150 million people by 1980 under the present practices. In this century, the pollution load from industrial wastes has soared from the equivalent of untreated sewage of 15 million people to 150 million. For 1970, the estimated figure is 300 million.

This tremendous acceleration in the discharge of waste products dictates a massive effort just to keep pollution at its present state, let alone decrease it. It means closing more beaches, higher costs to the home owner for water brought from greater distances, the disappearance of fish from nearby streams, and an increase in hepatitis and other waterborne diseases, possibly including cancer. Even if we could begin a massive cleanup campaign today, it might take as long as ten years merely to bring the water pollution level back to where it is today. In short, we're already dangerously late in our battle against water corruption.

The air pollution prospects are not only dismal, they are horrendous. A recent report by the Conservation Foundation says that the carbon dioxide content of the atmosphere has increased from about 290 parts per million in 1890 to about 315 at present. At this rate of increase, there is concern that within 200 years the average surface temperature of the earth could increase some 12 or 13 degrees Fahrenheit, since the carbon dioxide in the atmosphere has a greenhouse effect on the earth. An increase even half this great, according to that report, "would be more than sufficient to cause vast changes in the climate of the earth; the polar ice caps would almost surely melt, inundating many densely settled coastal areas, including the cities of New York and London . . . and many life forms would be annihilated both on land and on sea."

Carbon dioxide is not the only gas increasing in the earth's atmosphere. Vernon MacKenzie, Chief of the Division of Air Pollution Control of the Department of Health, Education and Welfare, has estimated that the increase of sulfur dioxide due to the burning of fossil fuels is so great that about one-third of all existing atmospheric sulfur is man-made. This one-third will surely increase with time, and the problems of health and property damage described earlier will accelerate.

Recent Public Health Service figures have shown that from 1950 to 1960 the number of people in the United States who lived in locations that had air pollution problems increased from 81 million to 104 million. By 1970, at the present rate of increase, 150 million persons will be living in areas with air pollution problems. The amount of combustible refuse, the number of motor vehicle registrations, the use of motor fuels, the number of manufacturing establishments, and the gross national product are proportionately increasing even more rapidly than our population.

The most serious acceleration consists of increased photochemical smog. It has been reported that the "nuisance" level of photochemical smog had been reached in our fourteen largest metropolitan areas by 1961, and that by 1975 the "acute" stage will exist in at least nine of the fourteen.

These numbers mean that air pollution, which was once considered to be an unpleasant but rare problem, is now a common aspect of our environment. They mean that killer smogs may eventually attack most large American cities. They mean that the incidence of respiratory diseases will continue to rise drastically. Already many New Yorkers smoke the equivalent of two packages of cigarettes a day over and above their voluntary consumption. This is more or less true in Los Angeles, Chicago, Boston, Detroit, Philadelphia, and Washington.

In short, currently serious air and water pollution problems are rapidly getting worse and will have reached the calamitous stage in the next ten to fifteen years. If government and industry do not move rapidly and vigorously, environmental pollution could be as great a menace as would be the radioactive debris of a total nuclear war.

Chapter 14

goals for government

THE PREVENTION and abatement of pollution require increased action at all levels of government. Effective control programs are best planned and enforced by authorities who are in a position to deal with contamination in its entirety. Often this will be at a local or regional level, but many of the major pollution problems can only be solved by the state or Federal governments.

The goals of pollution legislation should be the maintenance of public health and welfare, the protection of plant and animal life, the protection of property, the ensurement of safe visibility for air and ground transportation, together with continued economic development. At all levels of government, control is most effective when the supporting legislation is based on sound technical criteria and provides sufficient flexibility to be tailored to local conditions, including the structure and practices of state and community administration. Standards, codes, rules, and regulations governing the emission of pollutants should reflect such considerations as topography, meteorology, industrial development, urbanization, land use, and aesthetics. The key to successful pollution control, however, is the administration of rules and regulations, and it is therefore essential that there be specific designation of the agencies responsible for the various aspects of air and water pollution.

At the municipal level, there should be air pollution ordinances to control the most obvious sources of corruption. Even in a small community, action can be taken to outlaw the open burning of garbage, refuse, and junk, and to eliminate most odors from chemical operations. The use of backyard incinerators can be banned and replaced by a communal incinerator. In this case, however, municipal officials must be sure that their own system of waste disposal does not itself cause a pollution problem. Leaf burning can also be stopped by ordinance—if a leaf removal service is established. Finally, the small municipality can play an important role by establishing liaison with county and state control agencies for technical assistance and advice on existing or potential problems.

Larger communities require programs of much broader scope. Here emission standards for every major source of air pollution within the city limits should be established and enforced through a system of inspection and legal action. To do this, the city must appropriate sufficient funds to create an air pollution department large enough to carry out these functions. This involves adequate staffing, testing and monitoring equipment, engineering skills, and legal talent. A network of stations can be set up throughout the city to monitor pollutants such as dust-fall and sulfur dioxide. Comparison of this information with an emission inventory of the local industries makes it possible for competent engineers to pinpoint the sources of effluents. There should also be a system of permits for combustion equipment and a group of engineers which is capable of evaluating plans to detect potential pollution problems.

In cities where coal is the major fuel used for space heating, residential emissions create a serious problem. A substantial reduction in pollutants, such as occurred in Pittsburgh and St. Louis, is possible through large-scale conversion to gas or oil heating units. Backyard incineration is another significant source of residential pollution. In Denver it accounts for 25 percent of the local air contamination. One-third of New York City's air pollution is generated by 12,000 residential incinerators. The solution to these problems is the development of centralized municipal or private incinerators equipped with precipitators. Eliminating apartment house and backyard incineration will not only substantially reduce dustfall, it will save a community considerable money, especially if combustible wastes can be utilized as a fuel to make steam and electricity.

Fortune magazine estimates it would cost $60 million to modify 12,000 private incinerators if New York City develops an effective abatement campaign. On the other hand, construction of a city incinerator system would require only $15 million for the plant and an additional $19 million annually for service to eliminate 99 percent of the solid effluents presently generated by private incineration. This would reduce New York's total air pollution by about 30 percent. If the capital equipment costs were written off over a ten-year period, the total additional expense to individual New Yorkers would be 25 cents per month.

Water pollution is easier to control at the local level because major waste discharges are relatively few. The simplest municipal measure that can be initiated immediately is a prohibition of any new septic systems within city limits. There are few, if any, locations within municipal boundaries today that cannot be served by sewers connected to a waste treatment plant. Where septic tanks can still be justified, they should be limited to lots of at least an acre in size if exhaustive soil permeation tests indicate installation will not eventually create a health hazard.

Municipalities should plan to have separate storm and sanitary sewerage as soon as it is feasible. All new developments should be required to build separate systems. A municipality can set up a schedule to raise funds to convert existing systems. When possible, supplementary financing by the national government should be sought.

The construction of adequate municipal waste treatment plants and provision for proper operation should be undertaken by the city. Even more critical, immediate plans should be made to expand and improve existing facilities. Most cities now have serious problems because of near-obsolete systems. As a consequence, sizable expenditures will have to be made in the coming years. The city of Detroit, for example, will have to spend 100 million dollars to bring its sewage system up to standard. Cleveland has a 300,000-dollar study underway just to determine what must be done to upgrade the present sewage treatment facilities. Memphis will have to spend anywhere up to 80 million dollars to handle the 60 million gallons of raw sewage that it dumps into the Mississippi every day.

Although conservation of existing pure water does not strictly come under the heading of pollution control, it is a necessary and powerful tool in the fight against bad water. During the recent water shortage crisis, a cooperative New York City public proved that metropolitan water consumption can be reduced voluntarily as much as 20 percent. A more expensive and efficient approach would be to meter water and charge according to the amount consumed.

Finally, municipalities are often able to pioneer new approaches to pollution control. Santee, a San Diego suburb, is an outstanding example. Here a chain of small artificial lakes has been created from purified sewage. As it is sufficiently pure for fishing and swimming, this reconditioned water is a new recreational resource. The sewage is processed first by chemical treatment and then by underground injection to permit natural filtration by the soil.

Another successful pilot project in soil filtration without chemical treatment has been conducted at State College, Pennsylvania. There, aquifers have been replenished by the filtered sewage water. In addition to permitting reuse of the water, the soil utilized for filtration now yields larger and better crops than any nearby fields. The Penn State disposal system has been adopted by St. Charles in Maryland. Meanwhile, the Santee experiment is being studied by Los Angeles sanitary officials. Reuse of purified sewage is an inexpensive and technically feasible way of increasing pure water supplies on a large scale in many of our cities. It should get serious consideration by many more communities. The only major drawback is public reluctance to use treated sewage. In most cases, therefore, an educational campaign is necessary to overcome consumer resistance, and this may prove more difficult than the technological problems related to water purification.

Regional or metropolitan agencies to control both air *and* water pollution should be developed whenever possible. This approach has been extremely successful in the metropolitan Chicago area. There the sanitary district serves a large number of small communities in addition to the city of Chicago. The Metropolitan Planning Commission in the Chicago area is studying both air and water pollution to formulate an effective program of abatement and prevention. Citizens in the St. Louis metropolitan area have recognized the value of this approach by voting 214,800 to 39,000 in support of a 95-million-dollar bond issue for developing facilities to halt water pollution. As a result, the Coldwater Creek sewage treatment plant, built at a cost of 6,300,000 dollars in North St. Louis County, recently became operational. The plant is now converting a heavily polluted stream into a river suitable for recreation and eventually as a supply of drinking water. Even more important to that area was the enactment of a metropolitan sewer district ordinance that makes it illegal to discharge "any sewage, industrial waste, garbage, polluted water or any other material which constitutes a nuisance or hazard to the public health or welfare." This is an exciting measure, one which must be emulated in cities throughout the United States.

At the state level, the basic decision to carry out pollution control activity rests with the Governor and the State Legislature. Both must also be willing to allocate sufficient funds and impose the restrictions required for effective control. The state agencies can then take steps to define pollution controls. Thus, for example, a control board can forbid open burning, it can set up emission and water quality standards, it can require licensing of all new equipment capable of generating pollution, and, most important of all, it can enforce the control measure through an effective system of inspection and legal action against offenders.

Furthermore, it is highly important that state governments discontinue characteristically haphazard approaches to solving pollution problems. Once the major sources of existing and potential contamination have been identified, it is essential to plan a campaign to reduce pollution in an organized and logical way. This can be done if the state legislature sets up a commission to examine the problem on a statewide basis and to recommend a plan of attack which reflects available capabilities and resources. As air and water pollution are related problems, the plan should be an integrated attack on both fronts and administered by a single environmental contamination control agency. This entails such things as a proper allocation of funds over a span of several years, establishment of project priorities, designation of the type and allocation of treatment plants, and the specification of air pollution control equipment. Federal and state pollution control agencies should not be given responsibilities beyond environmental contamination. To do so dilutes their efforts and blunts their effectiveness.

A review of interstate pollution problems should have high priority on the agendas of state control agencies. Together with the neighboring state, an effective interstate agency should be established to handle the problem. This is a rather complicated procedure, since it requires the approval of the control bodies and the legislatures of each state. On the other hand, it permits respective state officials to solve their own problems before Federal action takes place. Now is a propitious time for undertaking such cooperation as the existing Federal legislation provides the largest share of available financing to the initiation of interstate organization.

The state can help solve the pollution problem that so often plagues the unincorporated areas within its borders. Environmental contamination in those locations frequently occurs because of the absence of clear authority by any governing body. The state legislature can assign to the township or county proper authority to deal with this. For example, in Cook County, Illinois, there are about 200 small municipalities in addition to the city of Chicago and the unincorporated areas. The County Board has air pollution jurisdiction over unincorporated areas but not over the 200 municipalities. In the absence of an effective agency, these small cities and villages have many unsolved air pollution problems. In this case, the Illinois State Legislature should grant to Cook County jurisdiction over air pollution throughout the area and provide sufficient funds to build a properly functioning staff. Other states in this country have similar jurisdictional problems that must be resolved by proper legislation.

Finally, standards for the discharge of pollutants into waterways should be established by each state. The Water Quality Act of 1965 allows the states two years to do this for interstate waters. State failure to meet the Act's water standards will result in Federal action. In many cases, state officials lack the mechanism necessary to set standards and should request assistance from the Federal government immediately. Where the state authorities are in a position to set proper standards, they should do so promptly and begin enforcement action at once.

Although giant legislative steps were taken by Congress in 1965, much remains to be done to control pollution on a national scale. This particularly applies to Federal funds available to states and cities for the construction of water waste treatment facilities. The present allocation of 150 million a year is grossly insufficient. Over the next ten years the construction of needed water treatment plants and the separation of combined sewers will cost between 25 and 50 billion dollars. Expenditure of this magnitude means that pollution control will have to become one of the major national objectives during the coming years. This is in line with the sentiments that have been expressed by President Johnson and Congressional leaders. The effect of pollution on our health, comfort, and economics leaves us no alternative.

The money allocated under the Clean Air Act to help states and cities build up their air pollution control staffs also will have to be increased considerably. The restriction of matching only new state or local allocations will have to be removed. Otherwise, state and local agencies will then find it necessary to cut their budgets drastically, since about two-thirds of the money used under the Clean Air Act will suddenly vanish when maximum support allowed by Congress has been reached. We do not advocate perpetual Federal financing of these agencies, but we do believe that a gradual withdrawal of Federal funds matched by increasing state or local money is the only logical way of preventing a wholesale decimation of their capabilities. This could be achieved by changing the ratio of Federal matching funds; first, a three-to-one ratio, then two-to-one, one-to-one, followed by a steady decrease in the ratio from the Federal side —one-to-two, one to-three, etc.—as a state activity grows.

Perhaps the most effective government role in pollution prevention thus far has been research on sources of pollution, on effects, and on improved methods for overcoming it. Most of the new information on pollution developed in recent years has come out of government laboratories or Federally supported research at private institutions. These efforts were expanded in 1965 with the allocation of money for the construction of a large research laboratory devoted solely to the study of automobile air pollution. It was established to develop emission standards and design new techniques for reducing the volume of pollutants. Federally supported research, both in air and water pollution, must continue and expand as it is the only feasible mechanism for maintaining the sizable and continuous effort. Additional attention should be given to procedures for translating new knowledge into action at every level of pollution control.

There is also a need for better communication with industry for the exchange of research information as well as coordination of research programs. A major effort at improving the working relationships between government and industrial research laboratories studying pollution problems should also be undertaken immediately. Government scientists and engineers should not be expected to solve individual industrial problems, but these are subjects of such magnitude that no single industrial concern can reasonably be expected to devote the money and manpower necessary for their solution. These research areas, together with causes, effects, and long-range fundamental problems, are appropriate areas of government research. Consequently, new solutions to pollution problems developed by the government should be widely published and made available for use by anyone in industry.

Another major successful and valuable government effort that should be continued and expanded is providing information and assistance to state and local control agencies. The knowledge built up by government experts is invaluable to newly organized control agencies. It can start them off with the benefit of the accumulated experience of other states.

Prompt installation of proper pollution control equipment by industry may cause companies to incur huge expenditures in a relatively short time. To encourage industry to install controls, a tax benefit should be applied to companies that voluntarily abate emissions. There is ample justification and precedent for this type of incentive. To ease this type of financial burden the government could allow special depreciations or write-offs, because it is in the national interest to reduce pollution and encourage industry to work with government rather than to fight legislative controls.

National government officials are also in the best position to draw up plans for control programs involving two or more states. The coordination of planning treatment plants on the shores of the Great Lakes, for example, is more logical than a haphazard, piecemeal approach by individual states. Even though implementation of pollution control is the responsibility of cities and states, the national government is best equipped with the manpower, funds and experience to determine the best approach to regional pollution problems.

Federal authorities should also be involved in developing preventive programs. Currently government action on interstate water or air pollution problems is cumbersome and belated. Only when the problem reaches calamitous proportions is the government allowed to exercise any abatement actions. By then it is usually far too late. Thus it is clear we sorely need legislation to permit early involvement at the government's discretion rather than by a summons from the affected states. Interstate pollution must be handled in the same effective manner as interstate commerce, for it is of similar importance and magnitude. Even more important, the government should be allowed to set up standards for interstate air and water pollutants and to enforce those standards. Representative Moss of California eloquently championed this position when he made the following statement that appeared in the April 28, 1965, issue of the Congressional Record:

> If clean water is our goal, it is essential that the Department of Health, Education, and Welfare be empowered to set standards of water quality not only to aid in the abatement of existing pollution, but to aid in the prevention of the further needless destruction of our remaining clean streams.
>
> In most of the 34 enforcement actions taken by the Department of Health, Education, and Welfare since 1957, water quality standards have been established by the conferees, or when necessary, recommended by the Secretary. There are at least 90 more areas where the Department of Health, Education, and Welfare has evidence of interstate pollution. If enforcement action is taken on these polluted streams, and if the Federal and state agencies must wait until each conference is held before establishing water quality standards it will be many long years before this pollution is abated. However, if the Department of Health, Education, and Welfare in cooperation with the state agencies can act now to establish water quality standards for interstate streams throughout the country, I believe that the course of remedial action could be clear to all, and pollution abatement could be accomplished more swiftly on the local, state, and Federal levels.
>
> Certainly water quality standards are an effective tool in pollution abatement programs, but even more important, they can be an effective measure in preventing pollution. Our scientists and engineers have developed almost miraculous techniques for reducing pollutants in waste discharges, but with all their technical knowledge and skill they cannot completely restore a filthy stream to its former freshness and beauty. The Potomac River is a good example of the deleterious effects of pollution on a once beautiful and clean stream. There is now an abatement program in force on the Potomac which will end the pollution of this river. But even with the tremendous efforts being put forth to clean up the Potomac, we know that the effects of the many years of pollution will not vanish overnight.
>
> The present approach of the Federal water pollution control program is negative. The Department of Health, Education, and Welfare under provisions of the Federal Water Pollution Control Act can act to abate interstate pollution only after health or welfare is endangered. In other words, the Department of

Health, Education, and Welfare can act only after serious and sometimes irreversible damages have occurred.

If the Department of Health, Education, and Welfare were able to set water quality standards, the Federal Government and the states could act to prevent the water quality from falling below these standards. Action could be taken before health or welfare was endangered and serious damages occurred. This is a positive, effective, and beneficial approach to preserving our water resources.

Since Representative Moss made this statement, the recent Congressional legislation described in Chapters 11 and 12 has improved the Federal position in establishing water and air quality standards. The procedures of setting standards are cumbersome, lengthy, and limited. Nevertheless, the principle of Federal responsibility for the quality of air and water has been established and will undoubtedly serve as a basis for future legislation.

The Federal government's position may be further strengthened as a result of President Johnson's message to Congress on February 23, 1966. His antipollution legislative requests for 1966 will include the following items:

1.   A program to clean and preserve entire river basins from their sources to their mouths by the adoption of water quality standards, adherence to them, and the provision of Federal funds to be used to match city and state funds for both planning and projects in this "Clean Rivers Demonstration Program".

2.   Federal support for state water pollution control agencies is to be doubled.

3.   The Water Pollution Control Act is to be amended to eliminate the two mandatory six-month delays.

4.   The Federal government is to be given authority to file suit immediately to stop pollution when that pollution constitutes an imminent danger to the public health or welfare, and additional legal strength is to be given to the government in these proceedings.

5.   The Federal government is to be allowed to initiate enforcement proceedings in both intrastate and interstate pollution.

6. All potential water pollution sources are to be registered, and the government is to have the right to inspect those sources.

7. Twenty million dollars are to be allocated next year for research in water pollution control techniques.

8. Added funds are to be requested from Congress for air pollution control research as well as for financial and technical assistance to cities and states.

9. Air pollution emissions from Federal installations are to be curtailed.

It is so important to become familiar with the pollution issues before Congress in 1966 that the recent Presidential message is presented in Appendix C at the end of this book. If enacted, the President's recommendations will substantially reduce environmental corruption, especially water pollution. These recommendations are for your personal benefit. They deserve your wholehearted support.

At the state level, only California has any semblance of an effective air pollution control mechanism. All others are either inadequate or nonexistent. Due to a water crisis, New Yorkers apparently are now willing to take water pollution seriously enough to attack the problem with vigor. Elsewhere (with a few notable exceptions) efforts to abate water contamination are feeble. Local air pollution control efforts are even more dismal. Of the hundreds of communities with serious air pollution problems, only Los Angeles and San Francisco have mounted a sizable effort. Even in these two outstanding cases, the annual volume of discharged aerial wastes continues to increase. It is evident that the activities, staffs, and budgets of government agencies at all levels must be substantially increased to abate the private, public, and industrial corruption of our air and water resources.

Chapter 15

a program for industry

"YOU MUST accept and act on the principle that the cost of pollution control from now on is part of the cost of doing business. If, and only if, the American business community acts on this principle, can we be certain that American business and America's communities will have the abundant supply of clean water that we need." This blunt message was delivered by James M. Quigley, assistant secretary of HEW at a national conference sponsored by the U. S. Chamber of Commerce. It was particularly directed to those executives who were apprehensive about the eventual effect of the new National Water Quality Act on their businesses.

Although this principle is not palatable to many, some industrialists do realize that the cost of air and water pollution control must be regarded as an intrinsic aspect of future capital equipment investment and operational costs. They probably realize that pollution abatement and prevention efforts often improve the economy and efficiency of their operations. Furthermore, voluntary steps to abate pollution prior to government action will usually improve a company's public relations with the community in which it is located. If voluntary industrial control is adopted, then logical and orderly solutions to pollution problems can be formulated. Naturally such programs will vary from industry to industry, indeed from one company to another, but certain basic steps are common to most or all of them. These consist of active antipollution measures at each plant through renovation of equipment or processes that are causing pollution, by designing all new equipment or processes to minimize emissions, by the joining together on an industry-wide basis for research on new control techniques as well as cooperative control measures, and through an active and positive role in local and national civic action.

The modification of existing equipment or processes to eliminate pollution is by far the most expensive, difficult and urgent step required. No one can reasonably expect industry to do this overnight. It is reasonable, however, to expect that major offenders should develop plans for pollution abatement and establish a realistic timetable for carrying out these plans. Acceptance of this policy by an industrial giant has already occurred. The DuPont Company had spent or authorized more than 91 million dollars in abatement facilities by late 1964.* It candidly pointed out that—"Despite this record, DuPont expects to spend many more millions keeping its problems under control. There is hardly a company plant where some problem does not still perplex; there is rarely a major process modification which does not require rethinking of the pollution abatement program at that particular site." This progressive point of view must be adopted throughout industry.

Chicago officials recently reached an agreement with industrial representatives to cut down dust from the steel mills within the city limits. As a consequence, Chicago steel firms plan to spend 30 to 50 million dollars on pollution abatement. This agreement has been hailed as an excellent example of how industry and government can work cooperatively. It may also establish a pattern for other cities to adopt. There is merit in these claims. Unfortunately, however, the agreement was a consequence of legal action by the city. It would have been to the industry's public relations interest to have taken action voluntarily.

---

* "Clean Air and Water In A Complex Society," DuPont Report No. 28, E. I. DuPont de Nemours & Co., Wilmington, Delaware, 1965.

Such an opportunity now exists in heavily industrialized northwestern Indiana. Eventually some legal authority will force the steel mills to clean up plant emissions. It would be an unparalleled gesture if the administrators of these mills voluntarily adopted action similar to the Chicago program. To do this on their own initiative, rather than being forced to do it, would gain them considerable good will, which eventually would more than compensate for the added cost of installing this equipment. Indeed, such recognition by industrialists is reflected in the plans now being developed along these very lines for steel mills in East Chicago, Indiana.

It has been estimated that the orange dust clouds emitted by steel mills could be eliminated from every steel mill in this country by the early 1970's at a total cost of about 500 million. The cost could also be calculated on the basis of $2.50 to $5.00 per ton of present capacity, a fee which could gradually be paid for by the consumer. The actual cost of cleaning up air pollution from the steel mills will probably be substantially higher, however, because it is unlikely that it will be done in the near future. Each year of delay will drive the eventual costs up.

The steel industry has been singled out above, but certainly it is not the only one that can take effective action to clean up pollution with the tools now at hand. A. J. von Fraank, representing the Manufacturing Chemists Association before the Muskie Subcommittee in its hearings on water pollution, pointed out that when the issue is tackled at the plant level, that is, individually, there are no staggering problems "other than the cost and the tailored adaptation of a broad spectrum of technologic tools to their solution. The chemical industry has a particular competence in the working of matter in all its forms and particularly in the separation of one kind from another, which in the final analysis is what pollution abatement is all about."

Members of the Manufacturing Chemists Association, which covers most of the industry, have invested 212 million dollars in air-pollution control facilities to date, and expect to invest another 49 million during the next five years. *Fortune*, in November, 1965, estimated that an expenditure of 250 to 500 million dollars for more pollution control equipment would raise the standards of all chemical plants to the level of the cleanest ones. It cites the case of phosphate fertilizer plants in Polk and Hillsborough counties in Florida (mentioned earlier in this book because of the effect of their fluoride emission on cattle). An equipment expenditure of 22 million during the past five years has cut emission in half while increasing production 43 percent. One company, faced with a shutdown by court injunction, managed to reduce its daily fluoride emission from 900 to 300 pounds in only 60 days.

The chemical industry also has water pollution problems that require abatement. It is estimated that new expenditures for this purpose are now running at a rate of about 15 million dollars a year and are increasing rapidly. Because of the nature of chemical manufacture, undesirable waste products are inevitable; dumping them into rivers and streams without thorough treatment cannot be tolerated.

Petroleum refineries can stop polluting the air, as has been shown by many cases in the Los Angeles area. The *Fortune* article speculated that the imposition of Los Angeles regulations would add only between five and ten percent to the cost of a new refinery. In 1961, U. S. petroleum refineries were spending about 18 million dollars a year on pollution-abatement equipment. Investment of another 10 million a year on equipment would soon bring them up to the highest existing standards. Part of this expense could be recovered by the sale of valuable chemicals that would be collected by control systems.

The petroleum industry has the same problem as the chemical industry in that it must concern itself as much with water pollution as with air pollution. Dayton H. Clewell, senior vice president of the Socony Mobil Oil Company of New York, has said that petroleum companies are spending about 30 million a year on waste water treatment with facilities valued at more than 250 million dollars. He predicted that outlays would be increased substantially in 1966. The pollution in the waters adjacent to our major refineries today lends mute testimony to this need for vastly increased spending for pollution control.

New electrostatic precipitators can remove up to 99.5 percent of the fly ash from coal burning by power plants. To achieve this level of control would cost the power industry about 300 million dollars—a figure that is estimated to have an effect of one percent on the price of electricity. *Fortune* estimated that if the power companies were forced to burn low sulfur coal or to install sulfur dioxide recovery systems in all new and existing coal stations, the total cost of the electricity generated by them would rise about 600 million a year. In the case of fuel oil, the technology does not appear to have advanced sufficiently to provide an economical method for sulfur dioxide elimination.

One corporate witness before a Senate Committee in 1964 estimated that it would cost industry 50 to 75 billion dollars a year to completely clean up the air. Industry can hardly afford to spend that much. Even if accurate, such an estimate should not serve as an excuse to ignore the problem. *Fortune* has estimated that a 3 billion dollar annual expenditure for air pollution control would be feasible and would effectively meet acceptable air quality standards. Although industrial efforts are now insufficient, expenditures for air pollution control have reached 300 million dollars a year. A tenfold increase, therefore, is not beyond reason.

The cost of substantially reducing water pollution by industry is also high. A reliable estimate is one billion dollars annually. Eventually, however, industrial expenditures would be significantly compensated by the profitable dividends accruing from the recovery of by-products and more efficient plant operation.

The ideal industrial approach is a preventive one consisting of designing and building plants so that the antipollution measures are incorporated right from the beginning. This approach is the most economic one for industry; it is also the most feasible one. While the renovation of existing plants to control pollution problems must, of necessity, be spread out over a number of years, the incorporation of control measures into new plants should start at once.

By the very nature of their respective responsibilities, industry and government are bound to differ on what reasonable pollution prevention equipment should be. Since the final decision as to the acceptability of such equipment will be made by government, it becomes apparent that very early in the game, industry should submit its proposed plans to government for approval. Government officials should decide whether the plans will meet whatever standards are in force or are likely to be required in the reasonably near future. If so, then industry has the right to expect that the standards will not be changed shortly after they have completed costly installations. If and when the requirements are made more stringent, due consideration should be given to industry's compliance at the time the plant was built and some sort of relief afforded to it.

On the other hand, if industry has not requested a review prior to the installation of equipment, government officials should not be in a position of having a moral obligation to go easy on industry because of money spent on capital equipment. Ideally, industry should take the initiative and present government with a set of plans for equipment it plans to install for pollution control. Government will then either approve the plans or tell industry how they should be modified to meet approval.

There are many ways in which industry and government can work together to combat pollution. These range from providing a forum for discussion of problems to working as a team on specific pollution problems. Probably the most frequently cited case of industrial and municipal cooperation to prevent water pollution is the joint effort undertaken by 2200 industries and 250 cities in the Ruhr Valley of West Germany. This group, called the Ruhrverband, oversees the use of the Ruhr River water. Since 1948 the water, which passes through what may well be the most heavily industrialized area in the world, has been cleaned and made potable by the construction of 102 water purification plants. The cost of plant construction has been defrayed by a system of dues paid by each of its members in direct proportion to the burden of waste that each member adds to the stream. This expense, as well as the desire to cooperate in making the water as clean as possible, has resulted in the development of internal recirculation systems by the steel mills so efficient that instead of using 130 cubic yards of water to manufacture a ton of steel, it now normally requires only 2.6 cubic yards of river water.

It can be argued that this situation is an unusual one, because German industry was rebuilt completely after having been devastated by warfare. It is therefore in a position to incorporate antipollution measures into new construction. That much is true. What is unique, however, is the assumption of responsibility for pollution by industry and government on a large scale. This collaborative action made possible a quick and effective cleanup of the Ruhr River.

It has been proposed by various authorities that a system similar to the Ruhrverband modified to local conditions could be set up along some of our major streams. The system would assess a fee against each industrial or municipal user proportionate to the cost required to clean up its waste by chemical treatment. The money raised in this manner would then be used to construct treatment plants. As an alternative, levying fees slightly above the cost of treating the wastes presumably would encourage the cities and industries to do the job themselves.

There are a number of groups sponsored by industry that are taking a very active role in pollution control. In many states they are helping to formulate and launch antipollution ordinances. A number of professional societies, sponsored by industry or with high industrial membership are active in disseminating information on pollution and how to prevent it. In addition, some companies sponsor research at various universities on particularly severe pollution problems. The value of such support is quite evident. Not only does it serve as gesture of public-spiritedness, but it also is a reasonable financial investment that could find methods of pollution control that would be cheaper and more effective than present techniques. As is so often the case with research, an initial expenditure of some money can eventually bring savings that exceed the expenditures. Here again, industry could cooperate quite well with government by making sure that the research it sponsors relates to government research without duplication.

Another type of industrial organization is the Oil Refining Companies' International Study Group For Clean Air and Water Conservation in Western Europe (CONCAWE). This group is made up of seven international oil companies. They pay membership fees in proportion to their share of Europe's oil refining capacity. CONCAWE has the following objectives:

1. Collation of information on the pollution of air, water and soil attributed to the oil refining industry;
2. Promotion of active cooperation between the participating companies toward finding ways to reduce pollution;
3. Provision of funds to research institutes for carrying out special studies;
4. Making available to other interested parties the results of these studies and the views of the organization.

A number of other organizations of this type could be mentioned here. For their own protection, as well as for the sake of cleaning up pollution, more industries should follow this approach. It cannot be stressed too strongly that these organizations must be constructive, not just apologists for existing conditions . We have already seen too much delay in the passage of pollution control laws by lobbying. The image of the industrial trade group has been tarnished in this way. Their policy and strategy must be altered so that they will become leaders rather than laggards in the fight against pollution.

Industry still has an opportunity to take a positive aggressive role in cleaning up and preventing pollution. It has the chance, and actually the duty, to lead the campaign by voluntarily installing equipment to end pollution. If it doesn't do so, then as surely as day follows night, the government will eventually force it to comply by vigorous legislation and legal action.

Chapter 16

civic action

THE MOST vital battles against air and water pollution must be fought in your own community. Federal and state programs can substantially aid municipal activities, but the key to success is cooperative action by citizens of the affected locality. When this occurs, as it did in Pittsburgh, the results are dramatic. There, a committee widely representative of the entire community drafted air pollution ordinances to clean up the smoke-burdened city. Reasonable time schedules were formulated for the achievement of definite objectives. Within a decade, almost 90 percent of all smoke was eliminated. In 1940, there were 1,000 hours when the visibilty in downtown Pittsburgh was less than three-fourths of a mile. By 1960 the time was reduced to 75 hours per year. The once-dying center of the city has been completely modernized and Pittsburgh now has an unparalleled economic boom as a direct result of a vigorous community program.

Unfortunately, civic action for air pollution control is rare. By contrast, community groups throughout the nation are striving to preserve clean water. In some cities they are supporting bond issues to construct sewage treatment plants. In others, they are encouraging the enforcement of antipollution ordinances or seeking passage of stronger local and state laws. In Charlotte, North Carolina, for example, the League of Women Voters coordinated a number of civic groups in support of a bond issue aimed at raising public funds for the improvement of the local sewage system. Prior to the election, an intensive voter education campaign was conducted. League members prepared slides, with a commentary, which were shown at four public meetings as well as to numerous civic groups. In this case, the bond issue passed by a higher margin than any other issue on the ballot.

The League of Women Voters put water resources on its agenda back in 1956. Clean water is now a "continuing responsibility" for League chapters from coast to coast. League spokesmen have testified before Congress in behalf of a comprehensive national program on water pollution. Groups in various regions have cooperated in programs of community education and legislative action to achieve interstate coordination in solving river basin problems.

Recently, under a grant from the U. S. Public Health Service, the League helped plan three "Seminars for Community Leaders on Land and Water Use for Tomorrow's Living." The meetings were held in the Connecticut River basin, the Southeast, and in the Lake Erie basin. Each seminar brought some 40 participants under one roof for three days to discuss area land and water problems. They represented such varied groups as bankers, garden club members, builders, insurance men, conservationists, industrialists, and local political officials. Speakers from government, business, universities, and conservation groups gave highlights of each basin's problems, needs, and potential. Available tools and programs for aid were outlined by experts. League speakers concluded the seminars by describing ways to get the facts, create public interest, draw in other community groups, interview public officials, and to set up meetings, TV shows, and citizen survey or action committees. League members from the areas in which the seminars were held recruited, mapped out a local program, obtained speakers, and made physical arrangements.

Water pollution is also an item of top priority for the General Federation of Women's Clubs, which adopted a resolution at its 1963 annual convention urging a stronger stand on the problem. In many regions, clubs are conducting education and action programs on water pollution. In the East, development plans for the Delaware River Basin are being studied; in the Southwest, members are attacking problems of soil erosion, threats to wildlife, and inadequate water supplies; in the Pacific Northwest, clubs are studying the Columbia River drainage basin and its water pollution problems. These women's club are arranging "show-me" trips, community conservation workshops, surveys of area problems, and contacts with local and state officials to support needed ordinances and legislation.

Conservation groups, historically, have been a leading force in water pollution control. The Izaak Walton League of America has as its principal objective "Clean Water for All America." As defined by its Executive Director, William Riaski, "the League's basic objectives involve promoting a better understanding of the principles underlying public resource programs . . . to inform private concerns, public administrative agencies, and elected bodies about the public interest in any particular public resource matter. We believe that, ideally, all water should be fit for direct human use without special treatment. We will be promoting this general concept through educational programs along with any specific resolution on which our membership decides." *

Other conservation groups in the fight include the National Wildlife Federation, National Audobon Society, Wilderness Society, Wildlife Management Institute, Sport Fishing Institute, and Outboard Boating Club of America. Local affiliates of these groups have initiated countless clean water campaigns of all kinds, and frequently collaborate with other organizations in community-wide efforts.

Many Junior Chambers of Commerce have adopted "Clean Water" action programs as part of their civic activities. They are following the lead of the Connecticut chapter which initiated a statewide program to alert all their communities to the problems of pollution. A Jaycee group in upper New York spon-

---

* "A Conservationist Views Water Pollution," *Industrial Water Engineering*, December, 1965, Vol. 2, No. 12.

sored an awareness-type program to stimulate local community action in ridding the Mohawk River of municipal and industrial wastes polluting it. Jaycees are adopting this responsibility because they believe that adequate treatment is absolutely necessary for attracting new industry and for growth in competition with other cities. They realize that waste treatment investments are as necessary as the installation of new machinery.

On the national scene, the work of 36 major conservation organizations is coordinated through the National Resources Council. Through publications, newsletters, exhibits, films, and meetings, these groups alert their own members and members of other organizations to the need for fighting pollution on all fronts.

The effectiveness of concerted action was demonstrated in 1962, when a 95-million-dollar bond issue was presented to St. Louis voters for the construction of plants to treat the raw sewage and industrial wastes being poured into the Mississippi River. A "Keep Clean Water" committee was formed with the cooperation of the entire business, labor, and civic community which conducted a widespread campaign. Intensified the month before election, the drive included developing newspaper articles, radio and television feature programs, door-to-door visits, and intensive publicity among all local clubs and societies.

Organizations that supported the campaign were the Chamber of Commerce, Conservation Federation of Missouri, Metropolitan Real Estate Board, Home Builders Association, Labor Council, Consumers' Federation, League of Women Voters, Missouri Federated Garden Clubs, Metropolitan Church Federation, Archdiocesan Council of Catholic Men, Rabbinical Association, as well as medical societies, Congressmen from the area, and all top officials and candidates. Nearly a million pamphlets and leaflets were distributed, some in shopping centers and others in schools for children to take home to their parents. Posters were placed in buses, streetcars, and store windows. These efforts resulted in the approval of the bond issue by a vote of 214,000 to 39,000—an overwhelming five to one ratio.

By adapting similar programs to the special problems and

needs of your community, your organization can successfully tell the citizens what pollution is, how it harms community progress and endangers health, and what must be done to control and prevent environmental pollution.

You need not belong to an organization, however, to contribute to pollution control. As voters and consumers, individuals have more influence than they suspect, and even a letter to your state representative or Congressman can be helpful. Furthermore, you can reduce your personal pollution by proper maintenance of your furnace and automobile and careful use of water in your home. Reporting pollution violations is also an important civic service. This has been extremely helpful to the Chicago Department of Air Pollution Control which received 34 percent more complaints during the first three months of 1965 than in the same three months of the preceding year.

"The news media in Chicago are to a large extent responsible for the public's cooperation and concern," said James V. Fitzpatrick, who, until recently, directed the air pollution department. "More and more people recognize the threat to health, blight of beauty, and damage to property caused by air pollution. The problem has become one of the major issues of our time."

This was not the case in the spring of 1959 when Laura Fermi, widow of the renowned physicist, Enrico Fermi, returned to Chicago after a visit to Europe. She was appalled at the dirt and soot she found in her home. Gathering a sample of the grit that had collected on her back porch, she submitted it for analysis to chemists at the Armour Research Foundation (now named IIT Research Institute). They found that it consisted of 10 percent unburned coal, 75 percent cinders and fly ash, and 15 percent dirt or dust. This led Mrs. Fermi to conclude that most air borne filth in her neighborhood was of local origin. As she has stated, until then she and her friends "had shared the prevailing attitude that in a large industrial city like Chicago filth is inevitable; either we accepted it or we went to live in the suburbs (dirt is listed as one of the three major causes for the exodus from the city); at any rate there was nothing we could do as individuals. But then we rebelled."

Mrs. Fermi and six women friends formed the Cleaner Air Committee of Hyde Park-Kenwood. Their first aim was to educate themselves about air pollution and its specific problems as related to Chicago. They were spurred on by the suspicion that in addition to the frustration involved in just keeping their homes clean, breathing dirty air probably also had an undesirable effect on the health of their families.

The women learned the basic facts about air pollution from their alderman, and then gathered more information through intense talks with the director of the Department of Air Pollution Control, scientists at IIT who were measuring dustfall throughout the city, doctors at Billings Hospital on the University of Chicago campus, the head of the local janitors' union, and members of the coal and oil industry. They soon learned that the main sources of particulate matter in their neighborhood came from poor combustion of heating and garbage disposal equipment, coal deliveries, ash removal, autos, unpaved lots, and miscellaneous street dirt. Only seven percent of the time were winds blowing in pollutants from the steel mills to the southwest. The women obtained copies of the city's air pollution control ordinance and with the assistance of a law professor reduced it to simple language. According to one expert they contacted, local vigilance could reduce dust and soot by some 20 percent; another claimed that full compliance with the ordinance would reduce city dirt by 40 percent. The most pertinent and specific provision of the regulations, for the purposes of Mrs. Fermi and her friends, was the one limiting smoke emission from buildings. It defined smoke densities and specified the time limits of the various emissions.

From the beginning, two approaches were advocated by the group. Some members hoped to obtain voluntary compliance with existing regulations through education and good will. Accordingly, they established personal contacts with large real estate holders, including the University of Chicago, and distributed material suggesting the proper care of heating and garbage disposal equipment as well as automobiles. Mrs. Fermi's group also prepared a pamphlet entitled, "Cleaner Air for Our City,"

which presented the air pollution problem, explained the city
ordinance, and suggested methods by which citizens could help
with its enforcement. This booklet was published and financed
by the Citizens Information Service of the League of Women
Voters. Within a few months 8,000 copies were distributed. An
additional 10,000 copies were underwritten by Kenneth V.
Zweiner, chairman of the Chicago Air Pollution Control Committee.

The more realistic women felt that enforcement could only be
obtained through sustained action against violators of the ordinance. As Chicago had only a handful of inspectors to cover
the entire city at that time, they recruited volunteers in the
Hyde Park-Kenwood area and trained them in smoke watching,
using a chart to determine smoke density. They also devised a
mimeographed report sheet on which the volunteer watchers
could jot down the address of an offending chimney and describe
the duration of its smoke violation. These were then sent to the
city's air pollution control department for investigation. The
Hyde Park Herald reported their activity was "the latest thing
in spectator sports in the Hyde Park-Kenwood area. It is similar to bird-watching, but where the bird-watcher uses binocu-
lars, the chimney-watcher uses a smoke (miniature Ringle-
mann) chart to indicate the degrees of blackness of the smoke."
The Cleaner Air Committee volunteer file now has some 200
names from an area of about 125 blocks, mostly housewives who
are eager to reduce the dirt in their daily lives.

Early in the fall of 1961, Mrs. Fermi's group launched their
second air pollution campaign. They reserved a booth in the
Hyde Park Shopping Center where they approached shoppers
and discussed pollution individually. For the occasion, children
painted posters and the women lugged boxes of literature to the
booth. Grocery-laden shoppers stopped to ask questions and pick
up complaint forms. In this way more literature was distributed and more volunteers recruited than at any previous formal
group meeting.

The main stumbling block to the group's effectiveness is the
fact that the air pollution department cannot take legal action

against a violation unless one of its trained inspectors has seen it. He alone can testify in court. Complaints call the inspectors' attention to certain buildings, but even the worst offenders do not smoke all of the time. In some cases, janitors only burn their garbage at night. Despite these legal obstacles, however, an informed and aroused citizenry can get results. One chronic offender in the neighborhood spewed black smoke and soot several times daily on adjacent new townhouses. After more than 100 complaints had been filed, the owner of the offending building was apprehended by an inspector and summoned to court. Twenty neighbors took an entire morning from their jobs to attend the trial of the landlord to witness his being fined 250 dollars and ordered to install new heating equipment.

Another result of these activities is that the Hyde Park-Kenwood neighborhood is now air-pollution conscious. Dirt, furnaces, auto emissions, and respiratory diseases are the topic of conversation at the most sophisticated parties. Small children point out smoking chimneys to their mothers, and school children strive to earn Cleaner Air Committee ribbons at an annual art contest. Mrs. Fermi believes there has also been material improvement, "that coal dust on windowsills is not as heavy, and rings around bathtubs not as black."

The ladies have certainly been instrumental in getting the Chicago City Council to pass stricter antipollution regulations and in the creation of a statewide air pollution control board. They have even helped influence Federal legislation. At a Chicago hearing of Senator Muskie's committee on air and water pollution in January of 1964, Mrs. Chauncey D. Harris, acting as spokesman, described the antipollution activities of their group, and concluded her testimony with this statement:

> Five years ago we began our fight against air pollution because we were weary of the dirt. Today we are continuing our fight because we feel that the evidence is becoming overwhelming, that our health and that of our children demand it.
>
> The Cleaner Air Committee of Hyde Park-Kenwood, representative of a grassroots citizen movement, strongly urges enlarged Federal, state, and municipal programs for the reduction of air pollution. We call upon other citizens to join in the effort to

make life more confortable and healthful for the citizens of the future.

In response to her remarks, Senator Bayh of Indiana commented,

>   I think one thing we recognized since the inception of our hearings has been the fact that one of our major problems with air pollution is the lack of public awareness.
>   It is my opinion, Mrs. Harris, that your interest and the interest of your group, and the interests of many other groups like it in your community and around the country are going to determine whether we are successful or not, because the members of this committee are determined to take whatever steps we possibly can. However, legislative effort and particularly its implementation are almost always contingent upon the determination of the local citizens and the local improvement associations.

Chapter 17

the crucial question

PUBLIC INFORMATION and education about air and water pollution are essential to the effective control of environmental corruption. While everyone cannot be expected to have a technical understanding of the problem, it is vital that most Americans have a broad comprehension of the magnitude and impact of the silent assault. Ignorance and indifference are the greatest barriers to achieving the President's objective of a beautiful and prosperous nation. It must also be emphasized that the responsibility for striving toward the optimum use of our vital resources rests inescapably on each one of us, whether we be government officials, scientists, industrialists, businessmen, professionals, laborers, students, or housewives. No useful purpose is served by name calling, blame fixing, or buck passing. *We are the enemy*, each of us, in the war against unnecessary wastes to our environment because we are generally doing little or nothing to abate unavoidable emissions and effluents. It is clearly our individual responsibility to take whatever action is feasible.

Within this framework, we must learn as much as possible about the conditions in our own community. With the facts in hand, we then can individually contact city, state, or national officials in person or by letter to express concern and to support adequate pollution control measures. It is not necessary to wait for specific legislation or a crisis to contact a government official or to circulate a petition. The individuals to whom you should write are listed in the appendices at the end of this book. It can be effective simply to express your views on the need for better environmental control even though it may result in higher taxes.

It cannot be overemphasized that expressing a viewpoint and then taking action accordingly is the proper exercise of one's civic rights. In the final analysis, this function is even more crucial to a healthy and vigorous democratic society than voting. Unfortunately, fewer Americans engage in political action than vote and little more than 50 percent of eligible voters bother to cast a ballot every two years. Few of those who do vote are well informed about either political candidates or issues. To a large extent, this lethargic and irresponsible approach to political activity is the seed out of which grows moral, political and environmental corruption.

After ignorance and apathy, financing is the major hurdle for a pollution control program. Even in California, where there is fairly broad understanding of auto emission hazards, a statewide effort to put crankcase blowbys on all used cars was abandoned because owners stubbornly resisted spending 25 dollars for such a device. Recently the Opinion Research Corporation revealed that 63 percent of the people queried on a nationwide basis said they were unwilling to pay anything at all to reduce water pollution. On the other hand it is encouraging to note that 29 percent expressed a willingness to spend as much as 100 dollars a year for cleaner water. Millions of families spend far more for such "necessities" as dishwashers, clothes driers, radios, television sets, powered lawn mowers, and wristwatches, to name a few from a long list of common commodities. Currently, as a nation we spend over 7 billion dollars on tobacco and some 15 billion for alcoholic beverages. These too, for many, are "necessities" that apparently are more important than health and welfare.

Efforts by individuals, civic groups, industry, and government to correct environmental abuses, however, are merely initial steps in assuming responsibility for the integrity of our natural resources. A more prudent and economical approach is the development of mechanisms for detecting potential hazards and preventing pollution before it begins. Many communities today do not have a pollution problem that requires immediate action, but the day is rapidly approaching when few will be free of damaging or objectionable pollutants. Government and civic leaders across the nation should now plan for that day, otherwise they will face the pressures and inefficiencies of "crash programs." This is an expensive and burdensome approach, unfortunately now essential in most large metropolitan areas, major river basins, and the Great Lakes area.

The opportunity is now at hand to study pollution problems and to avoid their consequences through urban renewal and development in cities throughout America. In the midst of demolishing old structures, redesigning transportation systems and reconstructing urban centers, we should pause to consider the effect on the quality of air and water. Traffic patterns, the location of industrial operations, the type of combustion systems and fuels, the equipment used in manufacturing, and the methods employed in disposing both liquid and solid wastes are aspects of metropolitan development that will affect the quality of air and water supply for future generations.

Astute planning will require a considerable increase in our research efforts. The need for research, however, whether it relates to existing or potential problems, must not be used as an excuse for delaying action now. Anyone who has been involved with pollution legislation knows that research is one of the favorite tools in political gamesmanship. Research becomes an end in itself for those who really don't want to take action, and they can always think up endless questions that deserve further study before considering the passage of a bill. As Senator Harrison A. Williams of New Jersey pointed out, "This is not to say that research is not important . . . But research is worthless unless it is accompanied by a desire and a determination to translate the fruits of it into action."

Once the scientific evidence has been presented, the establishment and enforcement of air and water standards becomes a social and economic problem that usually must be resolved by political and legal processes. Scientific endeavors have great potential power to serve society, but no amount of information will suffice if it is not available to the American public, to those who function as the final arbiters of national goals. Knowledge of environmental problems, therefore, and the willingness to explain them to the public should be a prime responsibility for every expert on the subject of pollution.

Although pollution experts and journalists stress health hazards and economic losses due to emissions and effluents, as we have in this book, there are other valid reasons for cleaning up the environmental mess that now exists in this country. They are more or less esthetic in character and relate to the human desire for beauty and pleasure. Certainly, the most obnoxious aspect of contamination is the generation of foul odors that plague urban air and most of our major highways. The sight of murky waters laden with refuse and feces can be more offensive than the stench itself. Municipal ordinances prohibiting roadside litter are not based on medical evidence that it is dangerous to human health, nor do home owners mow their lawns to prevent illness in their families. Esthetic considerations, in fact, may justify pollution control measures even more than health hazards and maintenance costs. We must, therefore, aim at and work toward the development of an environmental ecology that deals with human activities and enterprise and harmonizes them with our natural legacy. To this end we must employ the scientific talent, technological skills, finances, and political mechanisms that are essential to restoring the integrity of our vital resources. This is both reasonable and possible. It should also be our moral obligation, a responsibility not just to ourselves but to our children as well as to the generations that follow them. As Wallace Stegner expressed it, "Not life itself —not yet—but the satisfaction, and in Mr. Johnson's phrase, quality of life, is what we move to preserve."

As Stegner notes, most Americans think of conservation simply as a matter of preserving parks and open space, "the keeping or creating of antidotes to the industrial society that as

modern men we depend on and as natural creatures we loathe."
This is not enough. We cannot afford to attack each menace on a
piecemeal basis and then only when they take the shape of an
impending disaster. In Stegner's words:

> As President Johnson suggested in his Natural Beauty
> speech, and as Secretary of the Interior Stewart Udall has been
> saying for five years in his campaign to dramatize what he calls
> the quiet crisis, conservation cannot even save open space unless
> it concerns itself with the total environment. The 'land ethic'
> that Aldo Leopold called for in *The Sand County Almanac,* the
> sense of responsibility to the renewable earth, is in itself hardly
> enough. We need an environmental ethic that will reach all the
> way from the preservation of untouched wilderness to the beau-
> tification of industrial cities, that will concern itself with saving
> the still-savable and healing the half-ruined and cleansing
> the polluted, that will touch not only land but air and water, that
> will have as its purpose the creation of a better environment for
> men, as well as the creation or preservation of viable habitats
> for the species that our expansion threatens.*

We are now aware of the magnitude of pollution. At last we
realize how it is ravaging our health, wealth, and the beauty of
our once resplendent continent. We finally realize that our
technical and financial resources are adequate to the task before
us. The facts are in. Now is the time for action. Now is the
time for each of us to ask and answer the crucial question.
What are we now going to do—individually and collectively—
about the degradation of our air and water resources, about the
irresponsible and undefensible corruption of our environment?

Saturday Review, Vol. XLVIII, No. 20, May 22, 1965.

state pollution control centers

For each state the name and address of the organization responsible for pollution control is listed, as well as the identity of the director, so that concerned citizens can correspond directly with the proper officials.

Alabama

Arthur N. Beck, Technical Secretary
Water Improvement Commission
State Office Building
Montgomery, Alabama

Arthur N. Beck
Chief Engineer and Director
Department of Public Health
Bureau of Sanitation
State Office Building
Montgomery, Alabama

Alaska

Amos J. Alter, Chief
Branch of Environmental Health
Department of Health & Welfare
Alaska Office Building
Juneau, Alaska 99801

Thomas R. McGowan, M. D.
Acting Director
Department of Health and Welfare
Alaska Office Building
Juneau, Alaska 99801

Arizona

Director
Bureau of Sanitation
State Department of Health
State Office Building
Phoenix, Arizona 85007

William J. Moore, M. D.
Commissioner of Public Health
State Department of Health
State Office Building
Phoenix, Arizona 85007

Arkansas

Marvin L. Wood, Director
Water Pollution Control Commission
921 West Markham
Little Rock, Arkansas

M. L. Wood, Director
Pollution Control Commission
1100 Harrington Avenue
Little Rock, Arkansas

California

Paul R. Bonderson, Executive Officer

162

State Water Pollution Control
Board
1416 9th Street

Sacramento, California
John A. Maga, Chief
Bureau of Air Sanitation
Department of Public Health
2151 Berkeley Way
Berkeley, California 94704

Colorado

William N. Gahr, Director
Environmental Health Services
State Department of Public Health
4210 East 11th Avenue
Denver, Colorado 80220

Joseph Palomba, Jr., Chief
Air Pollution Section
State Department of Public Health
4210 East 11th Avenue
Denver, Colorado 80220

Connecticut

William S. Wise, Director
Water Resources Commission
State Office Building
650 Main Street
Hartford, Connecticut

Louis J. Proulx, Jr., Chief
Air Pollution Control Section
State Department of Health
79 Elm Street
Hartford, Connecticut 06115

Delaware

John C. Bryson, Director
Delaware Water Pollution Commis-
sion
State House Annex
Governor's Avenue & Division
Street
Dover, Delaware 19901

Floyd I. Hudson, M. D., Chairman
Air Pollution Authority
State Board of Health
Dover, Delaware 19901

District of Columbia

William H. Cary, Jr., Associate
Director for Environmental Health
Department of Public Health
401 Third Street, N.W.
Washington, D.C. 20001
Chief, Air Pollution Section
Bureau of Public Health Engineer-
ing
401 Third Street, N. W.
Washington, D. C. 20001

Florida

David B. Lee, Director
Bureau of Sanitary Engineering
State Board of Health
1217 Pearl Street
Jacksonville, Florida 32201

K. K. Huffstutler, Director
Polk-Hillsborough   Air   Pollution
Control District
State Board of Health
1217 Pearl Street
Jacksonville, Florida 32201

Georgia

R. S. Howard Jr., Executive Secre-
tary
Georgia Water Quality Board
47 Trinity Avenue, S. W.
Atlanta, Georgia 30334
Rudolph P. Lewis, Chief
Air Pollution Section
Department of Public Health
47 Trinity Avenue, S. W.
Atlanta, Georgia 30334

Hawaii

B. J. McMorrow, Executive Officer
Environmental Health Division
Department of Health
P. O. Box 3378
Honolulu, Hawaii

Leo Bernstein, M. D.
State Director of Health
Air Sanitation Section

P. O. Box 3378
Kinau Hale, Honolulu, Hawaii 96801

Idaho

Vaughn Anderson, Chief
Engineering & Sanitation Section
State Department of Health
422 State House, Boise, Idaho

Jess B. Hawley, Jr.
Department of Health
Air Pollution Control Commission
State House, Boise, Idaho

Illinois

C. W. Klassen, Technical Secretary
State Sanitary Water Board
616 State Office Building
400 S. Spring Street
Springfield, Illinois 62706

Clarence W. Klassen, Technical
Secretary
Air Pollution Control Board
616 State Office Building
400 S. Spring Street
Springfield, Illinois 62706

Indiana

Blucher A. Poole, Technical Secretary
1330 W. Michigan Street
Indianapolis, Indiana 46207

Perry E. Miller, Technical Secretary
Air Pollution Control Board
1330 W. Michigan Street
Indianapolis, Indiana 46207

Iowa

Paul J. Houser, Director
Public Health Engineering
State Department of Health
State Office Building
Des Moines, Iowa 50319

Paul J. Hourer, Director
Engineering and Industrial Hygiene
State Department of Health
State Office Building
Des Moines, Iowa 50319

Kansas

J. Lee Mayes, Chief Engineer
Division of Sanitation
State Board of Health
Topeka Avenue at Tenth
Topeka, Kansas

J. Lee Mayes, Director
Environmental Health Services
State Office Building
Tenth and Harrison Streets
Topeka, Kansas

Kentucky

Ralph C. Pickard, Director
State Water Pollution Control Commission
275 East Main Street
Frankfort, Kentucky

Dr. Russell E. Teague
Commissioner of Health
Air Pollution Program
275 East Main Street
Frankfort, Kentucky 40601

Louisiana

R. A. Lafleur, Executive Secretary
Louisiana Stream Control Commission
P. O. Box 9055, University Stream
Baton Rouge, Louisiana

John Trugg, Director
Public Health Engineering Section
State Board of Health
P. O. Box 60630
New Orleans, Louisiana 70160

Maine

Raeburn W. Macdonald, Chief Engneer

Water Improvement Commission
State House
Augusta, Maine

E. W. Campbell, Dr. P. H., Director
Division of Sanitary Engineering
Department of Health and Welfare
State House, Augusta, Maine 04301

Maryland

Robert M. Brown, Chief
Bureau of Environmental Hygiene
State Department of Health
301 W. Preston Street
Baltimore, Maryland

Howard E. Chaney, Chief
Division of Occupational Health
Bureau of Environmental Hygiene
State Department of Health
301 W. Preston Street
Baltimore, Maryland 21201

Massachusetts

Worthen H. Taylor, Director
Division of Sanitary Engineering
Room 511, State House
Boston, Massachusetts 02123

James L. Dallas, Chief
Air Pollution and Radiological
   Health Section
Division of Sanitary Engineering
Department of Public Health
Room 511, State House
Boston, Massachusetts 02133

Michigan

Loring F. Oeming, Executive Secre-
   tary
Water Resources Commission
Station B, Reniger Building
200 Mill Street
Lansing, Michigan

John C. Soet, Director
Department of Health
Division of Occupational Health

3500 North Logan Street
Lansing, Michigan 48914

Minnesota

Lyle Smith, Executive Engineer
Water Pollution Control Commis-
   sion
State Department of Health
University Campus
Minneapolis, Minnesota

F. L. Woodward, Director
Division of Environmental Health
Department of Health
Minneapolis, Minnesota 55440

Mississippi

Joseph E. Johnston, Director
Division of Sanitary Engineering
State Board of Health
P. O. Box 1700
Jackson, Mississippi

H. L. Vaughan, Director
Division of Occupational and Radiological Health
2423 North State Street
Jackson, Mississippi 39205

Missouri

Jack K. Smith, Executive Secretary
Missouri Water Pollution Board
112 West High Street
Jefferson City, Missouri

L. F. Garber, Chief Environmental
   Services
Missouri Division of Health
State Office Building
Jefferson City, Missouri 65102

Montana

C. W. Brinck, Director
Division of Environmental Sanita-
   tion
State Board of Health
Laboratory Building
Helena, Montana

John S. Anderson, M. D.

Executive Officer
State Board of Health
State Laboratory Building
Helena, Montana 59601

Nebraska
T. A. Filipi, Director
Environmental Health Services
State Department of Health
Box 4757, Statehouse Station
Lincoln, Nebraska

Nevada
W. W. White, Director
Division of Public Health Engineering
State Department of Health
755 Ryland Street
Reno, Nevada

E. G. Gregory, Chief
Bureau of Environmental Health
790 Sutro Street
Reno, Nevada 89502

New Hampshire
William A. Healy
Technical Secretary
State Water Pollution Commission
61 S. Spring Street
Concord, New Hampshire
Forrest H. Bumford, Director
Bureau of Occupational Health
State Department of Health and Walfare
61 S. Spring St.
Concord, New Hampshire

New Jersey
Alfred H. Fletcher, Director
Division of Environmental Health
State Department of Health
125 E. Hanover Street
Trenton, New Jersey

William A. Munroe, Chief
Air Sanitation Program
State Department of Health
P. O. Box 1540
Trenton, New Jersey 08625

New Mexico
Charles C. Caldwell, Director
Division of Environmental Sanitation
Department of Public Health
P. O. Box 711
Santa Fe, New Mexico

Edwin O. Wicks, M. D., Director
Division of Occupational Health-Air Pollution
Office of Environmental Factors
408 Galistco St.
Santa Fe, New Mexico 87501

New York
A. F. Dappert, Director
Bureau of Water Resources
State Department of Health
84 Holland Avenue
Albany, New York 12208

Hollis S. Ingraham, M. D., Chairman
State Air Pollution Control Board
84 Holland Avenue
Albany, New York 12208

North Carolina
Earle C. Hubbard, Secretary
State Stream Sanitation Committee
State Department of Water Resources
P. O. Box 9392
Raleigh, North Carolina

J. M. Jarrett, Director
Sanitary Engineering Division
State Board of Health
Raleigh, North Carolina

North Dakota

W. Van Heuvelen, Executive Officer
State Department of Health
Capitol Building
Bismarck, North Dakota

W. Van Heuvelen, Chief
State Department of Health
Environmental Health and Engi-
neering Services, State Capitol
Bismarck, North Dakota 58501

Ohio

George H. Eagle, Chief Sanitary
Engineer
State Department of Health
State Departments Building
Columbus, Ohio 43215

Jack A. Wunderle, P. E.
Engineer-in-charge, Air Pollution
Unit
Department of Health
State Departments Building
Columbus, Ohio 43215

Oklahoma

Loyd F. Pummill, Chief
Environmental Health Services
State Department of Health
3400 North Eastern
Oklahoma City, Oklahoma

Kirk T. Mosley, M. D.
State Commissioner of Health
3400 North Eastern
Oklahoma City, Oklahoma

Oregon

Kenneth H. Spies, Chief Engineer
State Sanitary Authority
P. O. Box 231
Portland, Oregon

Harold M. Patterson, Chief
Air Quality Control
State Sanitary Authority
State Board of Health

1400 SW. Fifth Avenue
Portland, Oregon 97201

Pennsylvania

Karl M. Mason, Director
Bureau of Environmental Health
Health & Welfare Building
P. O. Box 90
Harrisburg, Pennsylvania 17101

Victor H. Sussman, Director
Division of Air Pollution Control
Department of Health
P. O. Box 90
Harrisburg, Pennsylvania 17101

Rhode Island

W. J. Shea, Chief
Division of Sanitary Engineering
Department of Health
335 State Office Building
Providence, Rhode Island

South Carolina

W. T. Linton, Executive Director
Water Pollution Control Authority
Room 417, Wade Hampton Building
Columbia, South Carolina

South Dakota

Charles E. Carl, Executive Officer
State Committee of Water Pollution
State Capitol
Pierre, South Dakota 57501

Charles E. Carl, Director
Division of Sanitary Engineering
State Department of Health
Pierre, South Dakota 57501

Tennessee

S. Leary Jones, Director
Stream Pollution Control Board
727 Cordell Hull Building
Sixth Avenue, North
Nashville, Tennessee 37203

C. P. McCammon, M. D., Director
Division of Industrial Service
727 Cordell Hull Building
Sixth Avenue, North
Nashville, Tennessee 37203

Texas

David F. Smallhorst, Executive Secretary
State Water Pollution Control Board
1100 W. 49th Street
Austin, Texas 78756

Charles R. Barden, P. E., Director
Division of Occupational Health and Radiation Control
1100 W. 49th Street
Austin, Texas 78756

Utah

Lynn M. Thatcher, Executive Secretary
Water Pollution Control Board
45 South Fort Douglas Boulevard
Salt Lake City, Utah 84113

Lynn M. Thatcher, Director
Division of Sanitation
State Department of Health
45 Fort Douglas Boulevard
Salt Lake City, Utah 84113

Vermont

R. W. Thieme, Commissioner
Department of Water Resources
State Office Building
Montpelier, Vermont

Harry Ashe, Director
Industrial Hygiene Division
Department of Health

P. O. Box 333, 32 Spaulding St.
Barre, Vermont 05641

Virginia

A. H. Paessler, Executive Secretary
State Water Control Board
P. O. Box 5285
Richmond, Virginia

M. I. Shanholtz, M. D.
Commissioner of Health
Bureau of Industrial Hygiene
State Department of Health
Richmond, Virginia 23219

Washington

Roy Harris, Director
State Pollution Control Commission
409 Public Health Building
Olympia, Washington

Robert L. Stockman
Pollution Control Board
Air Sanitation and Radiation Control Section
1510 Smith Tower
Seattle, Washington 98104

West Virginia

Bern Wright, Secretary
State Water Resources Board
1709 Washington Street
East Charleston, West Virginia

Carl G. Beard, II
Executive Director
Air Pollution Control Commission
1724 Washington Street
East Charleston, West Virginia

Wisconsin

Theodore F. Wisniewski, Director
State Committee on Water Pollution
453 State Office Building

Madison, Wisconsin
O. J. Muegge, State Sanitary Engineer
Air Pollution Control Division

1 West Wilson Street
Madison, Wisconsin 53702

Wyoming
Arthur E. Williamson, Director
Division of Environmental Sanitation
State Department of Public Health

State Office Building
Cheyenne, Wyoming

Robert Alberts, M. D.
Acting Director, Department of
    Public Health
Division of Industrial Hygiene
State Office Building
Cheyenne, Wyoming 82001

Appendix B

city air pollution control

For representative cities throughout the country, the air pollution control organization is listed by name, address and telephone number. Also, the director or leading official is identified by name so that concerned citizens can address their questions or reports directly to a responsible individual.

California

San Francisco

Bay Area Air Pollution Control District,
1480 Mission St., San Francisco, Calif. 94103
Telephone: KLondike 2-1300
  Chief Administrative Officer...............D. J. Callaghan

Berkeley

Environmental Health,
Berkeley Health Department,
212 McKinley Ave., Berkeley, Calif.
Telephone: THornwall 1-0200, Ext. 274
  Chief.......................................Glenn Lynch

Fresno County

County of Fresno Department of Public Health,
Division of Laboratories and Division of Sanitation,
515 S. Cedar, Fresno, Calif. 93702
Telephone: CL 5-9711, Ext. 341
  Health Officer.......................Wm. A. DeFries, M.D.

Los Angeles County

Los Angeles County Air Pollution Control District,
434 S. San Pedro St., Los Angeles, Calif. 90013
Telephone: MAdison 9-4711, Exts., 66201, 66205, 66001, 66121, 66041, 66203, 66004, 66101
  Air Pollution Control Officer...............Louis J. Fuller

170

Orange County

    Orange County Air Pollution Control District,
1010 S. Harbor Blvd., Anaheim, Calif. 92805
Telephone: 774-0284
        Air Pollution Control Officer...............William Fitchen

Riverside County

    Riverside County Air Pollution Control District,
Health-Finance Building,
Room 234, 3575 11th St., Riverside, Calif. 92501
Telephone: 683-4000, Ext. 347
        Air Pollution Control Officer...........Charles J. Seymour

Sacramento County

    Sacramento County Health Department,
Air Pollution Control District,
2221 Stockton Blvd., Sacramento, Calif. 95817
Telephone: 454-2919
        Chief, Division of Air Sanitation.............Philip S. Tow

San Diego County

    San Diego County Air Pollution Control District,
Primary Health Center,
Civic Center, San Diego, Calif. 92101
Telephone: 239-7711, Ext. 631
        Director of Public Health and
           Air Pollution Control Officer...........J. B. Askew, M.D.

Delaware

Wilmington

    Department of Public Safety,
Bureau of Fire, Prevention Division,
Fire Station #4, 1200 King St., Wilmington, Del. 19801
Telephone: OL 2-0672
        Chief, Bureau of Fire....................Maurice K. Clark

Illinois

Bloomington

    City Manager's Office,
Monroe and East, Bloomington, Ill. 61701
Telephone: 967-6251
        City Manager...............................E. G. Moody

Chicago

    Department of Air Pollution Control,
Room 500, 320 N. Clark St., Chicago, Ill. 60610
Telephone: 744-4000, Exts. 4072, 4083, 4089, 4070, 3518.
        Acting Director........................William J. Stanley

Cicero

Air Pollution Commission,
4937 W. 25th St., Cicero 50, Ill.
    Chairman..................................Position vacant
    Secretary.....................................O. J. Cochran

Cook County

Cook County Department of Public Health,
329 S. Wood St., Chicago, Ill. 60612
Telephone: CHesapeake 3-5832, Ext. 64
    Chief Sanitary Engineer...................Robert deJonge

North Chicago

Department of Public Health,
City Hall, 1815 Sheridan Rd., North Chicago, Ill.
Telephone: DE 6-7700
    Chairman...........................Peter J. Stanul, M.D.

Indiana

East Chicago

Bureau of Air Pollution Control,
4525 Indianapolis Blvd., East Chicago, Ind. 46312
Telephone: 398-4200, Ext. 276
    Chief of Bureau..........................Dennis T. Karas

Evansville

Department of Smoke Control,
1065 W. Penn St., Evansville, Ind. 47708
Telephone: HA 4-6481, Ext. 258
    Smoke Commissioner and
        Combustion Engineer..................John E. Clausheide

Fort Wayne

Fort Wayne Department of Public Health,
337 E. Wayne St., Fort Wayne, Ind.
Telephone: 742-9302
    Health Officer......................Joseph H. Baltes, M.D.

Gary

Division of Air and Water Pollution Control,
3600 W. Third Ave., Gary, Ind. 46406
Telephone: 949-8486, -8487
    Chief.......................................Chris Angelidis

Indianapolis

Bureau of Air Pollution Control,
Room 1642, City-County Building,
200 E. Washington St., Indianapolis, Ind. 46204
Telephone: MElrose 3-3800, -3801
Superintendent and Combustion
Engineer.............................Raymond E. Wetzel

Michigan

Detroit

Bureau of Air Pollution Control,
Department of Buildings and Safety Engineering,
414 City-County Building, Detroit, Mich. 48226
Telephone: 965-4200, Ext. 501
Chief Air Pollution Inspector..............Morton Sterling

Flint

Division of Warm Air Heating,
City Hall, Room 210, 1101 S. Saginaw St., Flint, Mich. 48601
Telephone: CE 8-5641, Ext. 231
Heating Inspector...........................Harold Kirby

New Jersey

Bayonne

Department of Health,
City Hall, Bayonne, N. J. 07002
Telephone: FE 9-6900, Ext. 31
Director, Department of Health
and Welfare..............Joseph D. Mastromonaco, M.D.

Camden

Air Pollution Control, Division of Health,
Department of Health, Recreation and Welfare
City Hall, Camden, N. J. 08101
Telephone: WOodlawn 4-9000, Ext. 70
Health Officer....................Raphael Meadow, M.P.H.

East Orange

East Orange Health Department,
143 New St., East Orange, N. J. 07107
Telephone: 673-4100
Director, Air Pollution Control.....................Vacant

Elizabeth

    Department of Health,
    City Hall, Elizabeth, N. J. 07201
    Telephone: EL 3-6000, Exts. 30, 87
        Health Officer...........................George E. Laubach
        Air Pollution Inspector....................Joseph Faccone

Hoboken

    Board of Health,
    916 Garden St., Hoboken, N. J. 07030
    Telephone: SWarthmore 2-3000, Ext. 18
        Health Officer.............................M. R. Silon, M.D.

Jersey City

    Jersey City Department of Health and Welfare,
    Division of Health,
    City Hall, 280 Grove St., Jersey City, N. J. 07302
    Telephone: HEnderson: 4-3600, Exts. 35, 36
        Health Officer..........................Dennis J. Sullivan

Newark

    Bureau of Industrial Hygiene and Air Pollution Control,
    Department of Health and Welfare,
    Room 406, City Hall, Newark, N. J.
    Telephone: MItchell 3-6300, Ext. 441
        Supervising Chief......................Charles J. Maguire

New Brunswick

    Health Department,
    City Hall, 76 Bayard St., New Brunswick, N. J.
    Telephone: KIlmer 5-4700, Ext. 14
        Health Officer.............................John J. Hanson

Paterson

    Paterson Board of Health,
    20 Mill St., Paterson, N. J. 07501
    Telephone: ARmory 8-2110
        Health Officer................J. Allen Yager, M.D., M.P.H.

Perth Amboy

    Bureau of Air Pollution Control,
    City Hall, High St., Perth Amboy, N. J. 08861
    Telephone: Valley 6-0290, Ext. 2
        Director..............................Joseph J. Soporowski

Trenton

    Division of Health,
    Room 214, City Hall, E. State St., Trenton, N. J. 08608
    Telephone: EXport 2-3441, Exts. 34, 35, 36
        Health Officer...................H. Yale Tyler, M.D., M.P.H.

New York

Nassau County

Nassau County Department of Health,
Air Pollution Unit of the Division of Environmental Health,
County Office Building, 240 Old County Rd.,
Mineola, N. Y. 11501
Telephone: PIoneer 2-3000, Exts. 2930 through 2939
    Senior Air Pollution Chemist..................Leonard Feit

New Rochelle

Department of Public Health,
30 Church St., New Rochelle, N. Y. 10805
Telephone: NE 2-2315
    Public Health Engineer...............Stanley B. Stolz, P.P.

New York

Department of Air Pollution Control,
15 Park Row, New York, N. Y. 10038
Telephone: 566-2717
    Commissioner.................Arthur J. Benline, P.E.,

New York-New Jersey
Metropolitan Area

Interstate Sanitation Commission,
10 Columbus Circle, New York, N. Y. 10019
Telephone: JU 2-0380
    Director and Chief Engineer..........Thomas R. Glenn, Jr.

Poughkeepsie

Air Pollution Control Section, Fire Headquarters,
Little Washington St., Poughkeepsie, N. Y. 12601
Telephone: GLobe 2-0300, Ext. 1
    Inspector................................A. D. Sagendorph

Suffolk County

Suffolk County Department of Health,
Division of Environmental Health, Air Pollution Control Section
County Center, Riverhead, N. Y.
    Chief, Air Pollution..............William C. Roberts, P.E.

Syracuse

Bureau of Smoke and Air Pollution Control,
Department of Health,
415 City Hall, Syracuse, N. Y. 13202
Telephone: 473-4894, -4895
    Division Engineer.........................F. J. McArdell

Westchester County
>Department of Health,
>148 Martine Ave., White Plains, N. Y. 10601
>Telephone: WHite Plains 9-1300, Ext. 292
>>Director, Division of Environmental
>>Sanitation..............................R. M. McLaughlin

Yonkers
>City of Yonkers, Department of Health,
>Division of Environmental Health,
>87 Nepperhan Ave., Yonkers, N. Y.
>Telephone: YOnkers 3-3980, Ext. 246
>>Commissioner of Health..................Ralph Sikes, M.D.

Ohio

Akron
>Department of Health,
>Air Pollution Control Agency,
>502 Ohio Building, 175 S. Main St., Akron, Ohio 44308
>Telephone: 376-1431, Ext. 212
>>Director.............................Louis E. Bunts, P.E.

Cincinnati
>Bureau of Air Pollution Control and Heating Inspection,
>Department of Safety,
>2400 Beekman St., Cincinnati, Ohio 45214
>Telephone: 421-5700, Ext. 291
>>Air Pollution Control and
>>Heating Engineer.....................Charles W. Gruber

Cleveland
>Department of Urban Renewal and Housing,
>Division of Air and Stream Pollution Control,
>14101 Lakeshore Blvd., Cleveland, Ohio 44110
>Telephone: 486-1035
>>Commissioner..........................Albert W. Locuoco

Pennsylvania

Harrisburg
>Department of Public Safety,
>Health and Environment Sanitation,
>Room 214, City Hall, 423 Walnut St., Harrisburg, Pa. 17101
>Telephone: 238-7101, Ext. 215
>>Director...................................S. M. Stringer

Philadelphia City and County

Philadelphia Department of Public Health,
Community Health Services, Division of Environmental Health
Air Pollution Control Section,
500 S. Broad St., Philadelphia, Pa. 19146
Telephone: MUnicipal 6-5163
   Director, Division of Environmental
      Health...............................Arthur Wallach
   Chief, Air Pollution Control
      Section..............................Walter E. Jackson

Pittsburgh

Department of Health,
Bureau of Air Pollution Control,
626 City-County Building, Pittsburgh, Pa. 15219
Telephone: 281-4900, Ext. 776

Washington

Seattle

Department of Buildings,
503 Seattle Municipal Building, Seattle, Wash. 98104
Telephone: JU 3-2296
   Superintendent of Buildings.................Fred B. McCoy

Spokane

City Health Department,
221 N. Wall St., Spokane, Wash. 99201
Telephone: MA 4-4341, Ext. 232
   Health Officer...................Hampton H. Trayner, M.D.

Tacoma

Air Pollution Control Section, Division of Buildings,
Department of Public Works,
County-City Buildings, 930 S. Tacoma Ave., Tacoma, Wash.
Telephone: FUlton 3-3311, Ext. 469
   Air Pollution Control Engineer..............Joel L. Durnin

Appendix C

the president's message to congress

Albert Schweitzer said: "Man has lost the capacity to foresee and to forestall. He will end by destroying the earth."

The most affluent nation on earth may feel that it is immune from this indictment. A nation that offered its people—a century ago—uncharted forests, broad sparkling rivers, and prairies ripe for planting, may have expected that bounty to endure forever.

But we do not live alone with wishful expectations. We live with history. It tells us of a hundred proud civilizations that have decayed through careless neglect of the nature that fed them. We live with the certain future of multiplying populations, whose demands on the resources of nature will equal their numbers. We are not immune. We are not endowed—any more than were those perished nations of the past—with a limitless natural bounty.

Yet we are endowed with their experience. We are able to see the magnitude of the choice before us, and its consequences for every child born on our continent from this day forward. Economists estimate that this generation has already suffered losses from pollution that run into billions of dollars each year. But the ultimate cost of pollution is incalculable.

We see that we can corrupt and destroy our lands, our rivers, our forests and the atmosphere itself—all in the name of progress and necessity. Such a course leads to a barren America, bereft of its beauty, and shorn of its sustenance.

We see that there is another course—more expensive today, more demanding. Down this course lies a natural America restored to her people. The promise is clear rivers, tall forests and clean air—a sane environment for man.

I shall propose in this message one means to achieve that promise. It requires, first, an understanding of what has already happened to our waters.

The Pollution of Our Waters

"Pollution touches us all. We are at the same time pollutors and sufferers from pollution. Today, we are certain that pollution adversely affects the quality of our lives. In the future, it may affect their duration."

These are the words of the Environmental Pollution Panel of the President's Science Advisory Committee. They were written in November 1965.

At that time, every river system in America suffered some degree of pollution.

At that time, discharges into our rivers and streams—both treated and untreated—equalled the raw sewage from almost 50 million people. Animal wastes and waste from our cities and towns were making water unfit for any use.

At that time, rivers, lakes, and estuaries were receiving great quantities of industrial chemicals—acids from mine runoff—detergents and minerals that would not "break down" in the ordinary life of the water. These pollutants were re-entering domestic and industrial water supplies. They were killing fish. They posed hazards to both human and animal life.

By that time, on Lake Erie six of thirty-two public recreation and swimming areas had been closed because the water was unsafe for human beings. The blue pike catch in the lake had fallen from 20 million pounds in 1937 to 7,000 pounds in 1960. The oxygen that fish need for life was being rapidly devoured by blooms of algae fed by pollutants.

At that time, in the lower Arkansas Red River Basin, oil field development and irrigation were dumping salt into rivers. The result was an additional annual expense of $13 million to bring in fresh water.

I have placed these comments in the past tense not because they are no longer true. *They are more tragically true today than they were four months ago.*

I seek instead to make them a bench mark in restoring America's precious heritage to her people.

I seek to make them that point in time when Americans determined to resist the flow of poison in their rivers and streams.

I seek to make them ancient history for the next generation.

And I believe the conditions they describe can become just that—if we begin now, together, to cleanse our rivers of the blight that burdens them.

A Start Has Been Made

The first session of the 89th Congress launched a major effort to save America's water resources.

It authorized quality standards for all interstate waters.

It provided—in the Water Pollution Control Act of 1965— new resources for treating the wastes from our cities.

It created the Water Resources Council to coordinate all aspects of river basin planning. This unified effort promises to make the work of pollution control more effective.

We mean to make full use of these new instruments. They will require increased expenditures, in a year of few increases for urgent domestic programs. We shall make them.

Yet at this point the development of new knowledge, and new organizations to carry on this work, is as crucial as our dollars.

We must combine progressively all the means at our disposal —Federal, State, local and private—to reduce the pollution of our rivers.

A Clean Rivers Demonstration Program

I propose that we begin now to clean and preserve entire river basins from their sources to their mouths.

I propose a new kind of partnership—built upon our creative Federal system—that will unite all the pollution control activities in a single river basin. Its task is to achieve high standards of water quality throughout the basin.

The Clean Rivers Demonstration Program I recommend has four requirements:

1. Appropriate water quality standards—authorized by the Water Quality Act of 1965—must be adopted for every part of the basin.

2. The States and local communities must develop long-range plans to achieve those standards and to preserve them. The plans must be comprehensive, and they must be practical.

3. Where it does not already exist, a permanent river basin organization must be created to carry out the plan. It must represent the communities and the States. It must work closely with the Federal Government. The organization must be prepared to revise the plan as conditions require, so that new threats to the quality of the river may be turned back.

4. Communities must be willing and able to contribute funds necessary for constructing facilities. They must be prepared to levy charges for their use—charges adequate to maintain, extend, and replace them when needed.

The Federal Role

Federal financial assistance will be necessary if the Clean Rivers Demonstration Program is to succeed.

In most watersheds there are communities wholly without treatment facilities. There are some with only the most basic means for removing solid wastes.

Substantial funds will be necessary to construct the initial facilities. I therefore propose to:

eliminate the dollar-ceiling limitation on grants for sewage treatment facilities in these Clean River Demonstrations—but only in the Demonstrations.

provide special funds to finance both planning and project costs in Clean River Demonstrations.

In the first year, I am asking $50 million to begin this program.

To administer the program most effectively, we must reorganize the Federal effort. In the past, the Federal antipollution effort has been organizationally separate from water conservation and use programs.

One agency should assume leadership in our clean water effort. That agency should be the Department of the Interior. Today the Department's water management programs range from saline water research to irrigation. It is responsible for wildlife preservation, and for administering the National Park system. Its Secretary serves as chairman of the Water Resources Council. Thus its present task, and the logic of good government, require that it be entrusted with an important new effort to clean and preserve entire river systems.

I shall shortly submit to the Congress a reorganization plan to transfer to the Department of the Interior the Water Pollution Control Administration now housed in the Department of Health, Education, and Welfare.

Benefits of the Program

The program has one ultimate goal: to clean all of America's rivers. This year we shall start with those few basins whose States and communities are prepared to begin. As additional organizations are formed and their plans drafted, more basins will qualify.

The projects will be self-sustaining. Federal assistance is planned for the initial construction of local treatment works. Thereafter, local communities will collect revenues from users sufficient for the operation, expansion, and replacement of the facilities. Continuing responsibility will reside where the benefits accrue—with local authorities.

The projects will allow experiment with new forms of organization. State and local participation may be based on an interstate compact, a river basin commission, or even a conservancy district. The central requirement is for sufficient jurisdiction and authority to develop and carry out the long-range plan.

These projects will enable us to curtail and control pollution in entire river basins. Broad-scale planning of water standards in broad stretches of a river can achieve substantial economies. More efficient plants can be built to treat the wastes of several communities and nearby industries. Integrating the control of stream flow and treatment plant operation can reduce costs—for example, by fitting the type and amount of day-to-day treatment to varying stream conditions.

Our Established Programs

The Clean Rivers Program now holds great promise for restoring and preserving water quality. But in the beginning it can affect only a few areas. Our existing programs must continue. They must be improved—not only to help rescue other rivers from pollution, but because they provide the foundation for the river basin demonstration projects.

Federal grants for waste treatment plants now total more than $725 million. More than 6,000 projects are under construction or already completed. For Fiscal 1967 I have requested the Congress to appropriate $150 million, the full authorized amount, to continue this vital effort.

Under last year's act, the initiative for water quality standards rests, until July 1967, with the States. State governments now have an obligation to demonstrate their willingness and ability to control pollution. Some have already done so. The Federal Government must extend all possible help to enable the States to meet this responsibility. I am therefore recommending that support for State water pollution control agencies be doubled. The added amount should be used at the Secretary's discretion to assist States in devising effective water quality standards. It should be used to prepare plans for abating pollution.

Enforcement Authority

Standards, however, mean little without the power to enforce them. Existing Federal authority to abate water pollution is unnecessarily time consuming, complex in procedure, and limited in jurisdiction. Steps must be taken to simplify and strengthen these procedures.

I recommend that:

1. The Water Pollution Control Act be amended to eliminate the two mandatory six-month delays that unnecessarily burden its procedures;

2. The Federal Government have authority immediately to bring suit to stop pollution, when that pollution constitutes an imminent danger to public health or welfare;

3. More weight be given by the courts to the evidence produced in administrative enforcement hearings;

4. The Federal Government have the right to subpoena witnesses to appear at administrative hearings;

5. The Secretary be given the right to initiate enforcement proceedings when pollution occurs in navigable waters, intrastate or interstate;

6. Registration be required of all existing or potential sources of major pollution, and U.S. officials be given the right to inspect such sources; and

7. Private citizens be allowed to bring suit in Federal court to seek relief from pollution.

These are strong measures. But the menace of pollution requires them. It poses a major threat to the quality of life in our country.

Research for Comprehensive Pollution Control

The river basin proposals I am submitting take advantage of the best techniques available today. They apply new concepts of efficient organization. But if pollution control is to cope with increasing volumes of waste from our growing industry and population, new knowledge and technology are required. It is a challenge to research organizations, both private and public, to develop these technologies.

1. There must be new integrated systems of disposal. Many liquid wastes can be transformed to solids or gases—or vice versa. Research can show which form is least harmful and least costly. Research can reduce costs through combined solid-liquid disposal systems.

2. The technology of water treatment must be improved. We must find ways to allow more "re-use" of waste water at reasonable costs. We must remove or control nutrients that cause excessive growth of plant life in streams, lakes, and estuaries. We must take steps to control the damage caused by waters that "heat-up" after cooling generators and industrial engines.

3. More must be learned about the effects of pollutants and the present level of pollution. Better equipment must be developed to measure pollution load and movement. We must assess the results of particular pollutants on plants, animal, and human populations. We should continually monitor the quality of our environment, to provide a yardstick against which our progress in pollution abatement can be measured. We must apply the most modern techniques of systems analysis.

Such research will lead to pollution standards suited for each location and type of pollutant. It will permit us to direct our control efforts more efficiently. I am proposing that we spend over $20 million next year on this research.

Control of Air Pollution

The Clean Air Act of 1963 and its 1965 amendments have given us new tools to help attack the pollution that fouls the air we breathe.

We have begun to counter air pollution by increasing the tempo of effort at all levels of government.

In less than two years Federal financial assistance has stimulated a 50 percent increase in the air pollution budgets of States and local governments. Federal standards for the control of automobile exhausts will apply to the 1968 models. The Federal interstate abatement program will significantly supplement State and local efforts to deal with air pollution.

I am heartened by the progress we are making. But I am mindful that we have only begun our work. *I am forwarding to the Congress proposals to improve and increase Federal research, financing, and technical assistance to help States and local governments take the measures needed to control air pollution.*

Pollution from Federal Activities

The Federal government is rightly expected to provide an example to the nation in pollution control. We cannot make new demands on State and local governments or on private industry without putting the Federal house in order. We will take the necessary steps this year to ensure that Federal activities do not contribute to the deterioration of our water and air.

Last November I signed an Executive Order requiring that all new Federal installations include adequate water pollution control systems. Agencies are required to submit long-range plans to bring existing installations up to the high level of pollution control required of new facilities. The plans are to be submitted by July 1 of this year. We are providing the funds necessary to implement them.

I also intend to issue an Executive Order dealing with air pollution from Federal activities. The potential dangers of air pollution have only recently been realized. The technical and economic difficulties in conserving the purity of our air are, if anything, greater than in protecting our water resources. Nevertheless, I intend to see that the necessary steps are taken to curtail emissions from Federal installations.

Human Resources for Pollution Control

New projects and new technology are of little value without skilled people dedicated to putting them to effective use.

I propose to enlist the services of those in industry and the universities.

I propose to attract skilled administrators and scientists to the challenges of full-time occupations in pollution control.

Critical skills are in short supply in all public pollution control operations. We need to train scientists and social scientists in these activities, and to demonstrate the advantages of government service as a lifetime occupation. I propose to establish traineeships, fellowships, and an internship program in Federal pollution control activities. The participants will be in residence in Federal pollution control programs throughout the country.

Impact on our Cities

The Pollution Control programs I have recommended will benefit all Americans. But nowhere will the impact be greater than on our cities. These steps can clean the air that is today blighted by smoke and chemicals. These steps can bring to growing urban centers abundant supplies of pure water to sustain today's prosperity and to satisfy tomorrow's needs.

These steps can enrich the daily life of the city dweller and his children by restoring surrounding waterways to their unspoiled natural beauty. For we know that ugliness is degrading and costly, but that beauty can revive the human spirit and enlarge the imagination.

National Water Commission

In no area of resource management are the problems more complex—or more important—than those involving our nation's water supplies. The water shortage in the Northeastern United States is a dramatic reminder that we must take every possible step to improve the management of our precious water resources.

I propose the establishment of a National Water Commission to review and advise on the entire range of water resource problems—from methods to conserve and augment existing water supplies to the application of modern technology, such as desalting, to provide more usable water for our cities, our industries, and our farms.

This Commission will be composed of the very best minds in the country. It will judge the quality of our present efforts. It will recommend long-range plans for the future. It will point the way to increased and more effective water resource measures by the Federal Government, working in close cooperation with states, local communities, and private industry.

Saving our Forests

Since the century's beginning the national government has labored to preserve the sublime legacy that is the American forest.

Time after time public intervention has prevented the destruction of irreplaceable forest lands. Our National Park and Forest systems are America's principal trustee in the vital task of conservation. That task cannot be accomplished in a single stroke. It requires patient determination and careful planning to secure for our people the beauty that is justly theirs. It merits careful planning.

I propose that we plan now to complete our National Park system by 1972—the 100th anniversary of Yellowstone, the world's first national park. Substantial progress has been made during the last four years. Yet many scenic masterpieces remain unprotected and deserve early inclusion in the National Park system.

A Redwood National Park

I propose the creation of a Redwood National Park in northern California. It is possible to reclaim a river like the Potomac from the carelessness of man. But we cannot restore—once it is lost—the majesty of a forest whose trees soared upward 2,000 years ago. The Secretary of Interior—after exhaustive consultations with preservationists, officials of the State of California, lumbermen, and others—has completed a study of the desirability of establishing a park of international significance.

I have reviewed his recommendations, and am submitting to the Congress legislation to establish such a park. This will be costly. But it is my recommendation that we move swiftly to save an area of such immense significance before it is too late.

Other Outdoor Recreation Proposals

Other major outdoor recreation proposals which should be approved in 1966 are:

1. Cape Lookout National Seashore, North Carolina
2. Sleeping Bear Dunes National Lakeshore, Michigan
3. Indiana Dunes National Lakeshore, Indiana
4. Oregon Dunes National Seashore, Oregon
5. Great Basin National Park, Nevada
6. Guadalupe Mountains National Park, Texas
7. Bighorn Canyon National Recreation Area, Montana-Wyoming
8. Flaming Gorge National Recreation Area, Utah-Wyoming

For a region which now has no national park, I recommend the study of a Connecticut River National Recreation Area along New England's largest river, in the States of New Hampshire, Vermont, Massachusetts, and Connecticut.

I propose the early completion of studies and planning for two new parks—the Apostle Isles Seashore along Lake Superior and North Cascades in Washington State.

Nationwide Trail System

In my Budget, I recommended legislation to extend Federal support to the Appalachian Trail, and to encourage the development of hiking trails accessible to the people throughout the country. I am submitting legislation to foster the development by Federal, State, and local agencies of a nationwide system of trails and give special emphasis to the location of trails near metropolitan areas.

Preservation of Historic Sites

Historic preservation is the goal of citizen groups in every part of the country. To help preserve buildings and sites of historic significance, I will recommend a program of matching grants to States and to the National Trust for Historic Preservation.

Wild River System

I am encouraged by the response to my proposal for a National Wild Rivers system, and I urge the Congress to complete this pioneering conservation legislation this year.

Costs of Land Acquisition

The spiraling cost of land acquisitions by the Federal Government, particularly for water resource and recreational purposes, is a matter of increasing concern.

Land owners whose property is acquired by the Federal Government are, of course, entitled to just compensation as provided by the Constitution. At the same time, land for the use of the general public should not be burdened with the increased price resulting from speculative activities.

I have requested the Director of the Bureau of the Budget, together with the Attorney General, the Secretary of the Interior, and the heads of the other agencies principally concerned, to investigate procedures for protecting the Government against such artificial price spirals.

A Creed to Preserve our Natural Heritage

To sustain an environment suitable for man, we must fight on a thousand battlegrounds. Despite all of our wealth and knowledge, we cannot create a Redwood Forest, a wild river, or a gleaming seashore.

But we can keep those we have. The science that has increased our abundance can find ways to restore and renew an environment equal to our needs. The time is ripe to set forth a creed to preserve our natural heritage—principles which men and women of good will will support in order to assure the beauty and bounty of their land. Conservation is ethically sound. It is rooted in our love of the land, our respect for the rights of others, our devotion to the rule of law.

Let us proclaim a creed to preserve our natural heritage with rights and the duties to respect those rights:

> The right to clean water—and the duty not to pollute it.
>
> The right to clean air—and the duty not to befoul it.
>
> The right to surroundings reasonably free from man-made ugliness—and the duty not to blight.
>
> The right of easy access to places of beauty and tranquility where every family can find recreation and refreshment—and the duty to preserve such places clean and unspoiled.
>
> The right to enjoy plants and animals in their natural habitats—and the duty not to eliminate them from the face of this earth.

These rights assert that no person or company or government has a right in this day and age to pollute, to abuse resources, or to waste our common heritage. The work to achieve these rights will not be easy. It cannot be completed in a year or five years. But there will never be a better time to begin.

Let us from this moment begin our work in earnest—so that future generations of Americans will look back and say:

1966 was the year of the new conservation, when farsighted men took farsighted steps to preserve the beauty that is the heritage of our Republic.

I urge the Congress to give favorable consideration to the proposals I have recommended in this message.

LYNDON B. JOHNSON

THE WHITE HOUSE
February 23, 1966.